KU-167-392

quizactually

THE FESTIVE FAMILY FILM QUIZBOOK

quizactually

THE FESTIVE FAMILY FILM QUIZBOOK

Joe Shooman

jb

First published in the UK by John Blake Publishing
An imprint of The Zaffre Publishing Group
A Bonnier Books UK company
4th Floor, Victoria House
Bloomsbury Square,
London, WC1B 4DA
England

Owned by Bonnier Books
Sveavägen 56, Stockholm, Sweden

www.facebook.com/johnblakebooks
twitter.com/jblakebooks

First published in hardback in 2023

ISBN: 978 1 78946 712 3

British Library Cataloguing-in-Publication Data:

A catalogue record for this book is available from the British Library.

Design by www.envydesign.co.uk

Printed and bound in Great Britain by Clays Ltd, Elcograf S.p.A.

1 3 5 7 9 10 8 6 4 2

John Blake Publishing is an imprint of Bonnier Books UK
www.bonnierbooks.co.uk

To...,
Santa's Favourite Elf

Contents

Introduction ix
Arthur Christmas 1
Bad Santa 9
Batman Returns 13
Bridget Jones's Diary 19
Christmas Animations 27
Deck the Halls 35
Die Hard 39
Doctor Who Christmas Specials 47
Edward Scissorhands 53
Elf 57
Frozen 65
Gremlins 73
The Grinch 81
Harry Potter 85
The Holiday 89
Home Alone 97

It's a Wonderful Life 105
Jack Frost 111
James Bond 119
Jingle All The Way 125
Klaus 131
Krampus 139
Last Christmas 147
Love Actually 155
Miracle on 34th Street 161
The Muppet Christmas Carol 169
National Lampoon's Christmas Vacation 175
The Nightmare Before Christmas 179
The Polar Express 187
The Princess Switch 197
The Santa Clause 201
Scrooged 205
Shaun the Sheep: The Flight Before Christmas 213
Shrek 221
The Snowman 227
Star Wars Movies 235
Star Wars Holiday Special 245
Trading Places 249
While You Were Sleeping 255
White Christmas 259
Answers 263

Introduction

There's only one thing better than Christmas movies, and that's answering questions all about them. We therefore humbly present you with *Quiz Actually* – a title we totally thought up ourselves not related to any particular film or production. Oh, alright, you got us. But *Love Actually* is one of our favourite Chrimbo flicks, and you will be able to find questions about it on page 157.

Quiz, Actually comprises a mix of multiple-choice and straight-down-the-line questions; we like to mix it up around here. And, if that weren't enough, there's also all manner of challenges, forfeits, games, and fun activities – indeed, quite a lot of the time there's no need to have even watched the movie in order to have a good old-fashioned Xmas mess-about LOLtime.

The films are presented alphabetically – no favouritism here, despite what we just said above – and it's entirely up

to you whether you take it movie-by-movie and answer all the questions, or pick out the first three of different films, or just dive in and create whatever combination you feel inspired by.

There's enough here for the movie geeks to really go to town, as well as oodles of silliness – what better way could there be to tap into the season of good cheer?

Over to you...

Arthur Christmas

Ever wondered how Santa became Santa? Well, welcome to the world of Arthur Christmas – where Santahood is handed down generation after generation to those who are not just worthy but ready. Arthur Christmas is a modern folk-tale about technology, knowing your strengths and weaknesses, and good old-fashioned teamwork. As such, it could well be the perfect Xmas movie. But how well do you know this 2011 animation? Let's find out...

20 Questions

1. How many missions does a Santa usually undertake before passing on the title?

    a. 70

    b. 100

    c. 25

2. There have been a number of Santas before Malcolm. So what number Santa is he in the tradition?

    a. 5

    b. 20

    c. 200

3. What are the names of Malcolm and his wife Margaret's two kids?

    a. Adam and Steve

    b. Arthur and Martha

    c. Arthur and Steve

4. What is Steve's role in the operation?

    a. He is in charge of Mission Control at the North Pole

    b. He is in charge of matching up spare socks

    c. He has to clean up all the reindeer poo

5. And what about Arthur – what's his job at the start of the movie?

a. Dance instructor to the Elves
b. Head of the First Order
c. Replying to kids' letters to Santa

6. What happens when an elf accidentally presses a button?

a. The S-1 explodes
b. A present falls off the supply line
c. Santa turns purple and floats away

7. What is the name of the girl who is supposed to receive that present?

a. Glas
b. Gwyn
c. Gwen

8. And where does she live?

a. Trelew, Cornwall
b. Maesgeirchen, Bangor
c. Bigtown, Giantland

9. Why won't Steve use the S-1 to deliver the missing gift?
   a. He says it is out of petrol
   b. He says one gift out of billions is an acceptable mistake
   c. He does not like Gwen

10. Who comes to the rescue – or so he thinks?
   a. Grandsanta
   b. Grandstand
   c. Great Scott

11. Where does Arthur end up, though?
   a. The Isle of Man
   b. An island in Cuba
   c. At the South Pole

12. Steve does eventually take the S-1 to deliver a present – but what has he done wrong?
   a. He forgot that his feet were really stinky
   b. He forgot to lock the back door and all the snow came in
   c. He set the address to the wrong place, so the wrong kid got the present

13. Arthur, Grandsanta and the elf Bryony do reach England – but what happens to the sleigh?
    a. It is destroyed by a drone, because it is mistaken for an alien spaceship
    b. It falls to pieces because Grandsanta forgot to use washers when he was constructing it
    c. Nothing – it is magic so impervious to any damage

14. How do Arthur and Bryony escape?
    a. They take a magic bicycle ride with a passing wrinkly alien
    b. They click their heels together and make a wish
    c. They parachute to the ground safely

15. How do all the Clauses realise that Arthur deserves to be the new Santa?
    a. He fights them all with his special new powers
    b. He has given them all a Christmas bonus of £19
    c. He was the only one that cared about Gwen's Christmas

16. Gwen sees Arthur briefly, and he seems to have a beard – how so?
    a. It is made of snow
    b. Arthur has stuck cotton wool to his face
    c. Gwen needs glasses

17. At the very end, what is Steve's new job?
    a. Resident Cookie Eater
    b. Chief Operating Officer
    c. Chief of Police

18. And how about the elf, Bryony Shelfley?
    a. Minister of Funk (Bootsy Baby)
    b. Prime Monster (North Pole)
    c. Vice-President of Wrapping (Pacific Division)

19. What is the S-1 now called?
    a. EVIE
    b. STEVIE
    c. EFFOFF

20. Who sings the version of 'Santa Claus is Coming to Town' that plays over the final credits?
    a. David Hasselhoff
    b. Jar-Jar Binks and the Jedi
    c. Justin Bieber

Answers on page 264

Bad Santa

He knows when you are sleeping, he knows when you're awake, he knows when is the best time to thieve from department stores so answer these questions for goodness' sake... Yes, folks, it's everyone's favourite anti-Christmas movie. Billy Bob Thornton is brilliantly cast as the drunken, potty-mouthed safecracker under not-so-deep cover as a department store Santa. With a bunch of laughs, some splendid action scenes, a fair chunk of tugs-at-the-heart-strings and the unlikely-but-inevitable final redemption, Bad Santa is very much a modern Chrimbo movie. If you're sick of schmaltziness and snow-covered scenes of lovey-dovey Xmas films, this is an ideal way to re-set the heart-clock. But how well do you know the movie? Let's dive right in...

20 Questions

1. What is the scheme that Willie T. Soke and Marcus Skidmore put into play every year?
2. And who is the third member of the team?
3. What is the name of the manager of the mall in Saguaro Square, who Willie's foul mouth offends?
4. What attracts Willie to Sue at the bar?
5. What does Thurman Merman say his dad Roger was doing?
6. But where is Roger really?
7. Why does Willie end up moving into Thurman's house?
8. What gift did Thurman request from Santa, and what does he change it to?
9. And what have the bullies done to him?
10. What does Willie give Thurman, and why?
11. What present does Thurman give Willie?
12. What does Gin demand from Willie and Marcus?
13. But what drastic step do Marcus and Lois take?
14. How does Thurman respond when Willie tells him that he is not actually Santa?

15. What does Marcus reveal that he was planning to do to Willie?
16. What does Willie grab as he makes his escape?
17. But what happens just before he can reach Thurman's front door?
18. Why is Willie found innocent?
19. And what will Willie's new job be?
20. What is Sue's new role at the end?

Answers on page 264

Batman Returns

Nanananananananana BATMAN, Batman, Batmaaaaaan. Grumpy, rich, no particular special powers, but a massive following nonetheless. Did you know there's been more than one Robin? That sidekick's name alone makes Batman Returns *a Chrimbo movie...*

Riddle Me This

Name all the Christmas elements in *Batman Returns*. Convince your fellow players why this ought to be in the pantheon of Chrimbo films. The other player/s have the right to reply, of course: can they convince you that it *shouldn't* be an Xmas movie?

Which Batman?

Put the following Batmen (Batmans?) in order of Batman-ness.

Movie Stars

Christian Bale
Robert Pattinson
Michael Keaton
Val Kilmer
George Clooney
Ben Affleck

TV and Oldies

Adam West
Lewis G. Wilson
Robert Lowery

Rhetorical Question Time

As Bruce Wayne is so enormously rich, how come he doesn't just fund a working police department in the

first place? Where do his taxes go? And can one legally claim Batmobile maintenance against our taxes? These questions need to be answered!

20 Questions

1. The person that directed this movie has been involved with a few seasonally-set films – but what is his name?
2. Which actor plays Batman in this iteration?
3. And who plays Catwoman?
4. Which vertically-challenged actor embodies the Penguin?
5. What is the name of the gang that disrupts the tree-lighting ceremony?
6. And what is the name of the businessman kidnapped by the Penguin?
7. How does the Penguin become a hero?
8. And what is the Penguin's real name?
9. How does Shreck attempt to murder his secretary, Selina?
10. But she survives – how?
11. And what does she do at home in anger?
12. How does she plan to get her own back on Shreck?

13. Again she escapes a potentially fatal fall – how does she do it this time?
14. How does Batman sabotage the Cobblepot Rally and therefore the Penguin's mayoral race?
15. As a result, what does Penguin vow to do by way of revenge?
16. What is the technological ace that Penguin plays after Batman foils his Red Triangle Circus gang?
17. How many times is Catwoman hit by shots from Shreck's gun?
18. Catwoman then takes out the building, Shreck and (presumably) herself. How?
19. How does a desperate Penguin try and kill Batman, but fails?
20. Who do we see looking at the BatSignal at the very end?

Answers on page 265

Bridget Jones's Diary

Love, shenanigans, unsuitable dalliances and a surprisingly good if cliched English posh-ish accent from an unexpected source. Yes, folks, it's Bridget Jones's Diary, *and no Christmas would be complete without someone groaning that it's on telly and wanting to put the darts on instead...*

Discussion Time

Who owns the biggest pants in your party? What colour might they be, and how comfortable are they? No fibbing now!

What Would You Do

If you had two people who might be in love with you, how would you choose between them? Would your heart rule your head, or vice versa? What attributes would make you go weak at the knees? Would you set up a series of tasks for them to do in order to win your heart? And what would make them run away if you wanted them to get lost?

20 Questions

1. How old is Bridget at the start of the movie?
   a. 28
   b. 40
   c. 32

2. Which animal is on Mark Darcy's jumper at the New Year's Day buffet?
   a. A reindeer
   b. A cow
   c. An elephant

3. What is Bridget's New Year's Resolution?
   a. To learn to play trombone in the London Symphony Orchestra
   b. To take control of her life, beginning with keeping a diary
   c. To go wild swimming every morning in the Thames

4. How does Daniel try to put Bridget off Mark?
   a. By saying he is already married, in Australia
   b. By telling Bridget that Mark has outstanding financial convictions
   c. By saying that Mark had once slept with Daniel's then-fiancée

5. What was the original theme of the family party Bridget and Daniel are scheduled to go to?
   a. 'Tarts and Vicars'
   b. 'Star Wars'
   c. 'Brits and Yanks'

6. Daniel supposedly goes back to London for work. But what does Bridget find instead?
   a. Daniel and his mates playing *Would You Rather?*
   b. A naked Lara in Daniel's flat
   c. Two naked elves cavorting in Daniel's attic

7. What does she tell him she'd rather do than go back to work for Daniel?

   a. Paint the Forth Bridge with her underarm hair
   b. Work wiping Saddam Hussein's arse
   c. Watch *Love Actually* eighteen times in a row

8. At Bridget's dinner party, what colour is the soup?

   a. Green
   b. Red
   c. Blue

9. How does Mark describe the three courses?

   a. 'Blue soup to start, orange pudding to end, and, well, for a main course… congealed green gunge'
   b. 'Red soup for starters, yellow poo for a main course, and then an exploded butter cloud'
   c. 'Snail porridge to begin, then magic beans, and a golden egg for pudding'

10. Daniel turns up, drunkenly trying to win back Bridget. What does Mark say to him?

   a. 'You're a big man, but you're in bad shape. With me it's a full-time job'
   b. 'Daniel, I'm going to smack you right upside the kisser'
   c. 'I should have done this years ago'

11. Which European cuisine is served at the restaurant the two crash their way through?

a. German
b. Dutch
c. Greek

12. The fight seems to end, but what does Daniel say to Mark, that makes the latter come back and knock the former down?

a. 'I've got Bridget, and you're a loser'
b. 'Wanker'
c. 'Your moose jumper is shit'

13. What is the name of the TV presenter with whom Bridget's mum has a torrid affair?

a. Julian
b. Joseph
c. Jacaranda

14. Bridget seems to have chosen between her two potential suitors. But what is Mark scheduled to do instead?

a. Become a Shaolin monk and learn the secrets of the Kung-Fu masters
b. Take over Daniel's company and turn it into an executive gym
c. Move to New York to work and be with another woman

15. Where do Bridget's friends plan to take her to cheer her up?

   a. Center Parcs
   b. Paris
   c. Bangor

16. Before she can leave, Mark turns up – what does he say he'd forgotten to do?

   a. Kiss her goodbye
   b. Return her library books
   c. Update his passport

17. With Bridget changing into something sexier, what does Mark find which makes him leave?

   a. Her big pants
   b. Her collection of Tamagotchis
   c. Her diary

18. Bridget is disconsolate – he's gone! But when he reappears, what does he have?

   a. A new diary, so she can make a new start
   b. A Mogwai
   c. A first edition of *Trivium: The Mark of Perseverance*

19. Bridget says that nice boys don't kiss like that. What's Mark's reply?

a. 'I'm sorry, I was too forward'
b. 'Oh yes they fucking do'
c. 'I've never kissed a nice boy'

20. And which author wrote the original *Bridget Jones* books?

a. Helen Mirren
b. Harpo Marx
c. Helen Fielding

Answers on page 267

Christmas Animations

There's nothing better than sitting down with a box of chocs and watching some of the best animated shows on telly. But how much do you know about the (mostly) seasonal antics of the characters and plots of the programmes? From South Park *to* The Simpsons *and* Ice Age *to* Happy Feet, *here's a real selection box of questions to get chomping on.*

Challenge Time

Every player draws a three-panel cartoon about Christmas, using any characters you like. No need to be Rembrandt here – it's the theme and the vibe that count. Award marks for jokes, silliness, story, originality and anything else you agree on *before* you embark on the task.

Twist: Put a time limit on the exercise.

Fiendish Twist: Use an app/animation technique of your choice to animate your cartoon!

20 Questions

1. What kind of animal is Sid, in *Ice Age*?
   a. Sloth
   b. Squirrel
   c. Sabre-toothed Tiger

2. Can you name all six *Ice Age* full-length movies to date?

3. And what was the name of the 2011 Christmas special?

4. What was the name of the very first episode of *The Simpsons*?
   a. 'Simpsons, We're the Simpsons'
   b. 'Simpsons Roasting on an Open Fire'
   c. 'Fantastic Mr. Simpson'

5. In that episode, what second job does Homer take on?

a. Racecar driver
b. Middle-distance athlete
c. Mall Santa

6. How is Christmas saved?

a. Bart wins the lottery
b. Homer and Bart bring a dog home
c. Marge reveals she has already bought the gifts

7. In *Happy Feet*, what are the names of the mummy and daddy penguins?

a. Norma Jean and Memphis
b. Lisa-Marie and Elvis
c. Jehosephat and Gasbum McPlop

8. As a result of being dropped as an egg, Mumble cannot do what?

a. Sing
b. Jump
c. Swim

9. What is the name of the group that Mumble joins?

a. Maroon 5
b. Rabo de Toro
c. The Adelie Amigos

10. Which actor voices Mumble?
    a. Elijah Wood
    b. Kirk Douglas
    c. Stephen Mulhern

Bonus opportunity: Put on your favourite song and make up a new dance to it. Discretionary points from fellow players for originality, fun, and making people laugh.

11. *South Park* now, and an icky one to start with: what kind of creature is Mr. Hankey?

12. What is the name of the episode which features initially cute but ultimately murderous psychopathic forest creatures?
    a. 'Babes in the Wood – Tooled Up'
    b. 'Woodland Critter Christmas'
    c. 'Christ-pi-kay-ay, Woodland Critters'

13. Why does Ike have to leave South Park in the episode 'It's Christmas In Canada'?

14. In the *Family Guy* double-episode, 'Road to the North Pole', what is Stewie's plan?

15. But what is wrong with Santa?
    a. He is exhausted from trying to keep up with the demands for more and more presents
    b. He has broken his left foot by accidentally going down the chimney in the Eiffel Tower
    c. He has gone into retirement and intends to spend Christmas on Seven Mile Beach, Grand Cayman

16. Let's get back to less controversial animated entertainment. Do you know what year *A Charlie Brown Christmas* was first aired?
    a. 1985
    b. 1945
    c. 1965

17. And what is the name of the main cartoon strip the characters appear in?

18. Why is Charlie Brown upset?
    a. He has lost his favourite Christmas socks
    b. Christmas has become too commercial and people are being greedy
    c. He does not like the snow

19. But who is it that makes him happy about it again?

20. And at the lovely ending, with Charlie Brown's tree looking magnificent, what does the ensemble sing?
    a. 'Hark! The Herald Angels Sing'
    b. 'Mr. Blue Sky'
    c. 'Ace of Spades'

Answers on page 267

Deck the Halls

We're talkin' the 2006 movie here, folks – so put all the other ones outa your mind. We're planning to scan the depths of our online programme guides to count all the Chrimbo flicks that share the same name, but are in fact entirely different films. For this title, we've got at least three so fa-la-la-la-la, la-la-la-laaaaa.

20 Questions

1. Which diminutive star plays Buddy?
2. He once had a giant twin – who was that, and what was that movie called?
3. And who plays Steve?
4. In which movie did this actor once have a famous day off? What car was his dad's pride and joy?
5. Who does Buddy manage to sell a car to?
6. How does Buddy plan to make his mark, specifically using his house?
7. Steve's Christmas card photo is ruined. How?
8. What happens to his car?
9. And finally the Christmas tree area?
10. What does Steve do, to try and short-circuit the lights?
11. But what has Buddy already got in place?
12. Buddy and Steve make a bet. What is it?
13. Even so, what does Steve tell Buddy he has not achieved?
14. And how does Buddy try and finally attain that?
15. What is the name of the illegal firework Steve buys from a gangster?

16. But what does he hit with it instead of Buddy's house?
17. How has Buddy been powering his lights?
18. The two make friends – how do they bring their families back?
19. People turn up to try and re-fit the lights; when they do not work, what do people do?
20. When the lights are plugged in properly, what does MTV report?

Answers on page 269

Die Hard

Spoiler alert: he doesn't. We won't elaborate on whether we think it's a Christmas film or not, because it's so much fun to discuss. In fact, how about we start off with that always-controversial issue?

Gone in 60 Seconds

Speak for one minute, without deviating, hesitating or repeating yourself, on why *Die Hard* is a Christmas movie. Award yourself 100 points for lasting the whole minute. If you do not last the full minute, the number of seconds that have passed becomes your score, i.e. 42 seconds lasted = 42 points.

Face Off

Go head to head on the one-minute challenge – one arguing for, and one against, it being a Chrimbo film. (Not at the same time, obviously. The person with the longest trigger finger goes first.) Timed points apply.

Judgement Day

You can suspend the hesitation, tangents and repetition forfeit for this version.

The other players can form a panel and give points for how convincing each argument is (or isn't). This can be by writing down scores out of 10 secretly, and folding up the paper until the question's done, or alternatively by holding up scorecards at the time.

20 Questions

1. What is the name of the company that Holly McClane works for?
   a. Nintendo Limited
   b. Nakatomi Corporation
   c. Nick Knowles Incorporated

2. How does John McClane respond when the police supervisor tells him the line is for 'emergency calls only'?
   a. This is an emergency – I am dying hard here
   b. I didn't ring for advice from a goddamned desk jockey
   c. No fucking shit, lady! Does it sound like I'm ordering a pizza?

3. What is McClane's famous response to the thieves' boss Hans Gruber's taunting?
   a. Yabadabadoo, money funster!
   b. Yippee-ki-yay, motherfucker!
   c. That's what your mum said last night

4. Rather than being actual terrorists, what were the gang looking to steal?
   a. An ancient Inca gold icon
   b. Bearer Bonds worth $640 million
   c. The secret recipe for KFC

5. Which movie star does Gruber erroneously refer to when he says they will not walk into the sunset with Grace Kelly?

a. John Wayne
b. Clint Eastwood
c. Fred Astaire

6. All things being equal, where does McClane say tell Sergeant Powell he would rather be?

a. At home watching *It's a Wonderful Life*
b. At the North Pole with Santa
c. In Philadelphia

7. How does McClane deduce that the gang is mostly European?

a. They all wear Nordic sweaters
b. They are whistling songs by ABBA
c. Their clothing labels and cigarettes

8. Which sweet goodies does Sergeant Al Powell buy from the convenience store?

a. Cookies
b. Doughnuts
c. Twinkies

9. What is the name of the classical piece that is a recurring theme for the terrorists (and hummed by Gruber at one point)?

a. Beethoven's 'Ode To Joy'

b. Mozart's 'Eine kleine Nachtmusik'

c. Vivaldi's 'Summer' from *The Four Seasons*

10. What is the password for the vault?

a. Akira

b. Shakira

c. Akagi

11. What does McClane use as a visual reference to help him navigate the lift/air vents?

a. Graffiti that reads 'Stallone turned this role down'

b. A bulb that is flashing on and off

c. A *Playboy* centrefold

12. What is the name of the book that *Die Hard* is based on?

a. *Die Hard*

b. *Nothing Lasts Forever*

c. *The Very Hungry Caterpillar*

13. Which song can we hear at the end of the movie?
   a. 'Good King Wenceslas'
   b. 'Frosty the Snowman'
   c. 'Let It Snow'

14. What make is the watch that Holly has that ultimately seals Gruber's fate?
   a. Timex
   b. Casio
   c. Rolex

15. By whom was the movie distributed?
   a. Paramount
   b. 20th Century Fox
   c. Warner Brothers

16. *Die Hard* was nominated for four Academy Awards (Oscars) in 1989. How many did it win?
   a. 4
   b. 2
   c. 0

17. What were the names of the subsequent sequels?
   a. *Die Hard 2, Die Hard 3, Die Hard Another Day, Come Die With Me, Never Die Never Again*
   b. *Die Hard 2, Die Hard With a Vengeance, Live Free or Die Hard, A Good Day To Die Hard*

c. *Die Hard 2, Die Hard With Vegetarians, Give Me The Box, Die Harder Than This, Die-Face*

18. Which character did Alan Rickman go on to play in *Harry Potter*?
   a. Coriolanus
   b. Snake
   c. Snape

19. Roughly how much have the *Die Hard* movies collectively grossed, worldwide?
   a. $800 million
   b. $20 billion
   c. $1.5 billion

20. In 2007, to which museum did Bruce Willis donate John McClane's iconic white vest?
   a. Smithsonian
   b. National Movie Museum
   c. Rijksmuseum

Answers on page 270

Doctor Who Christmas Specials

Ah, the Whoniverse... Full of lovely angels and friendly cyber-people. A splendid place where everyone gets on famously and there's never, ever any kind of problems. Hang on, no, that's Tellytubbyland isn't it? Sorry, let's start again. The Whoniverse: what an incredibly dangerous and strange place it is. Here's a taster set of questions about some of the Chrimbo adventures of the Doctor her/himself...

20 Questions

1. Before the Noughties reboot, there was one special Christmas Day episode of *Doctor Who* aired. For a point each:

    a. What year was it?

    b. What was that episode called?

    c. Who played the Doctor?

Bonus: In 1981, there was a spin-off Christmas show for one of the then characters. Which character was it, what was the name of the programme, and what was the name of that episode?

2. Why is Earth particularly vulnerable at the start of 2005's 'The Christmas Invasion'?

3. How are the Sycorax controlling the humans?

4. Which six words does the Doctor whisper to Alex, that he claims could bring down Prime Minister Harriet Jones?

5. What was Donna Noble about to do in the 2006 Christmas special when she accidentally ends up in the TARDIS?

6. What is at the core of the Earth?

7. What is unusual about the Doctor as the Thames drowns the Racnoss?

8. What unexpected event begins 2007's 'Voyage of the Damned'?

9. Why is London deserted?

10. How does the Doctor try to save Astrid?

11. Which year is it at the start of 2008's 'The Next Doctor'?

12. And who are the villains in this episode?

13. How does the (real) Doctor vanquish their king?

14. In 2009, 'The End of Time' was the Christmas (and New Year) special. Who was resurrected as the baddie in this one?

15. What would the consequences of the return of Gallifrey to the universe be?

16. And what does the newly-regenerated Doctor shout gleefully right at the end of the two-parter?

17. Who played the Doctor in 2010's 'A Christmas Carol'?

18. What does Abigail's dial actually signify?

19. What is unusual about the creatures who lead Kazran and Abigail's sleigh?

20. Would you like a quiz book all about *Doctor Who*?

Answers on page 270

Edward Scissorhands

The gorgeously sad twisted fairytale is one of Tim Burton's very best – and also one of the strangest. It remains true to the genre of 'what if' storytelling, which is where the greatest fantasia can often be found. Is it a pure Christmas movie? Well, we're not sure; but we are sure that it's one of the most atmospheric, gothic, sweet, lovely, heart-tugging, slightly gruesome, and inventive movies out there. What do you think?

A World of Pure Imagination

Imagine you had to replace one of your body parts with a tool, like scissors instead of hands. What would you choose? Trowels for feet? Snakes for hair? A tongue made out of pliers? How would that make your life different? And what would be the advantages?

20 Questions

1. How come Edward has scissors instead of hands?
2. The inventor is a horror movie legend, and this turned out to be his final film role. What's his name?
3. Edward has been living alone for years. Who knocks on his door?
4. She takes him home to live with her family. Can you name them? Three points available.
5. How do they introduce Edward to the neighbours?
6. And what skilful work does Edward do to endear himself to them?
7. This develops into two other endeavours particularly suited to his special skills – what are they?
8. Who offers to help Edward open his own hair salon?
9. She scares him away. How?

10. Now Kim's boyfriend, Jim, asks Edward to do something that's more than a touch immoral. What?
11. Jim runs away and Edward is arrested. What do the police conclude?
12. Edward makes it 'snow'. How?
13. How does Jim ruin this?
14. And what does this cause Edward to do?
15. At the Boggs's home, a very upset Kim asks Edward to hold her. Does he do so?
16. Edward spills more blood in the Boggs family. How?
17. He then cuts Jim, whilst defending himself. What does Jim do?
18. Edward will not fight – until Jim does something unconscionable. What?
19. What does Kim tell the neighbours has happened to both Jim and Edward?
20. And what does the old lady storyteller reveal at the end of the movie? Extra points for extra details of the bittersweet wonderment here.

Answers on page 272

Elf

Grown man in an elf costume? Glorious amounts of very, very sugary food? Oodles of silliness? We're in like Flynn, baby. How can you not be a fan of this one?

Who am I?

- ★ Take some strips of paper, and write different characters from the movie on them. Fold them up and put them into a hat/bag/bowl.
- ★ Take it in turns – one player is active at a time.
- ★ The active player must take a piece of paper *but not look at it.*
- ★ Still without looking, they must stick the paper to their forehead, so everyone else can see who they are.
- ★ Note that these questions must have an answer that is either *yes* or *no*. For example: 'Am I a human?'; 'Do I wear a green suit?'; 'Do I work in Santa's toy factory?'; 'Am I an elf?'; and so on.
- ★ The winner is the one who guesses who they are the quickest!

Variation: *Everyone* takes a piece of paper, and plays as above, but can ask one question each in turn, going clockwise around the table/room.

Affirmative/Untrue

Also known as the *Yes/No Game*. One player picks a piece of paper, as above, and asks another player questions accordingly as to who they are. However, the player *being asked* must answer these questions without saying the words *yes* or *no*, and the questions can be open-ended ones (that is, the questions can have answers that are more elaborate than just yes and no).

20 Questions

1. Simple pimple first question: What's the name of Will Ferrell's character?
   a. Diddy
   b. Buddy
   c. Puff Diddy

2. But how did he become an elf in the first place?
   a. He crawled into Santa's sack as a baby
   b. He was on a work placement scheme
   c. He had magic powers from falling into a cauldron

3. And what does his biological father do?
   a. He is a street cleaner
   b. He is a politician
   c. He works at a kids' books publisher

4. What does our main elf say when he's told that Santa will be at the store the next day?
   a. 'I know him'
   b. 'He's my friend'
   c. 'His real name is Dave'

5. And what does he do to prepare for Santa's visit?
   a. Puts everything in alphabetical order
   b. Decorates the store overnight
   c. Opens all the windows to let snow inside

6. What whispered truth does he deliver to the store Santa when it's revealed it's not the 'real' Santa?
   a. 'You are a snotty faced poo bum'
   b. 'You make me a sad panda'
   c. 'You sit on a throne of lies'

7. What are the four main elf food groups?
   a. Candy, candy canes, candy corns, and syrup
   b. Presents, love, magic, and melody
   c. Vitamins, roughage, fat, and carbs

8. What good news is the main character delighted to relate to Michael?
   a. 'I saw a dog today'
   b. 'It's snowing'
   c. 'I have got five hundred credits on *PacMan*'

9. But how does he make fast friends with Michael?
   a. He is an absolute boss in a snowball fight
   b. He shows Michael the secret way to wrap presents very quickly
   c. He buys him a brand-new Mongoose BMX

10. Do you know how long the elf's famous belch lasts for?

    a. Five seconds
    b. Ten seconds
    c. Twelve seconds

11. Which actress plays the part of Buddy's love interest?

    a. Zooey Deschanel
    b. Zoe Wanamaker
    c. Zebedee Q. Hackysack

12. And what is her character's name?

    a. Jodie
    b. Jolene
    c. Jovie

13. What does Buddy specifically apologise for in his farewell Etch-a-Sketch note?

    a. 'I'm sorry I ruined your lives, and crammed eleven cookies into the VCR'
    b. 'I apologise profusely for the spaghetti stains on the television'
    c. 'I am so sorry about my stinky farts that woke you up because they were so loud'

14. Buddy gets attacked by a racoon, but what does he really want?

a. A conversation
b. A chat
c. A hug

15. What crashes in Central Park?

a. A roller-coaster
b. Santa's sleigh
c. Two roller-skating nuns

16. What is Buddy's unfortunate contribution to Walter's manuscript pitch?

a. He spills candy on it
b. He tells them it is a rip-off of *Bad Santa*
c. He puts it through a shredder to make 'snow', thus destroying it

17. What story does the elf suggest that Mr. Greenway loves?

a. *The Story of Santa*
b. *Tales of the Unexpected Presents*
c. *The Story of Buddy*

18. But what happens?
    a. Walter tells them to be quiet and go home
    b. Mr. Greenway decides to have a kebab instead
    c. Mr. Greenway is rude to Michael and Buddy, so Walter quits

19. How does Buddy prove that it is really Santa?
    a. He shows everybody Santa's passport
    b. He reveals what people have received as presents in the past
    c. He shows everybody his bulging sack

20. And in the end, what fixes the sleigh?
    a. Green Flag
    b. A special candy cane
    c. Everyone singing and getting into the Christmas spirit

Answers on page 273

Frozen

Simply iconic: one of the movies that absolutely swept all before it on its release, and it continues to delight fans worldwide. Snuggle up, folks, and let's melt our hearts as we magic ourselves into the Frozen *universe.*

Challenge

Everyone in turn must either perform a song from the movie, or an impression of one of the characters. Extra points for props, funny new lyrics, and ability to turn things into ice by magic.

If I Was

Imagine you have been granted one special power. What would it be? Would you use this magic for good, or to make yourself rich/famous/invincible? Who would be your main allies, and would you have a mortal enemy?

Drawing on Ice

Using coloured pencils/pens/crayons or whatever you have available, draw a brand new character that would fit into the *Frozen* universe. Name the character, give them a special power, and also give them a hidden weakness. What kind of creature will you create? Will they have colourful clothes/fur? Where will they live?

Extended remix: In the manner of *Dungeons and Dragons*, create a scenario in which these characters have adventures. You will need a dungeonmaster/storyteller to prepare first, and you may use dice et cetera as per *D&D* – depending how much you want to get into it! Alternatively, you may just have the characters meet each other. How would those conversations go?

Extension on the extended remix: Once you have ten or more new characters, name five different characteristics, for example Magic; Ferocity; Friendliness; Length of Wand; Snow-skills. Agree how many points out of, say, 100, each character scores on each of those characteristics.

Write these down on the character's piece of paper. Shuffle all the characters' papers together, and make sure each player is dealt the same amount of papers. (You might want to copy them onto more durable cards, but it's not essential.)

You can now play them against each other. Take it in turns to choose a characteristic that you think will be highest on your top paper/card. If it beats the other/s in play, you take their character into your own pile. Winner is the one who ends up with all the cards.

20 Questions

1. What is the name of the *Frozen* kingdom?
   a. Viennetta
   b. Artichokia
   c. Arendelle

2. And the name of the sisters?
   a. Anna and Elvis
   b. Anthony and Cleopatra
   c. Anna and Elsa

3. But who is older?
    a. Anna
    b. Elsa
    c. Elvis

4. What unexpected things does Olaf the snowman like?
    a. Warm hugs and summer
    b. Carrots and coal
    c. Drawing pictures of cattle

5. What is Kristoff's profession?
    a. Industrial Mowing Facilitator
    b. Ice Harvester
    c. Deer Hunter

6. And his reindeer mate's name?
    a. Seven of Nine
    b. Sven
    c. Seren

7. Surely we all know this one, but let's see! What song does Elsa sing whilst creating her icy palace?
    a. 'Peter Snow'
    b. 'Run To The Hills'
    c. 'Let It Go'

*Bonus points for **not** singing it at this point.*

8. Which troll helps Anna and Kristoff?
    a. Terence
    b. Bubba Ho-Tep
    c. Bulda

9. And what is her relation to Kristoff and Sven?
    a. She is their adoptive mother
    b. She is their schoolteacher
    c. She does not know them, and is a silly sausage

10. What does the Bishop ask Elsa to do which makes her nervous during the coronation?
    a. Take her gloves off – she starts to make the orb freeze by doing so
    b. Sixteen burpees without even telling anyone she's in training
    c. Go to collect three hundred Elf Coins from Mordor's Dragon Pit

11. What does Elsa tell Anna she knows nothing about?
    a. Car maintenance
    b. Trance music
    c. True love

12. Who runs the Trading Post and Sauna?
   a. Oaken
   b. Peken
   c. Queeken

13. On their way up to North Mountain, Anna, Kristoff and Sven's sled is attacked. Who or what by?
   a. A pack of hungry wolves
   b. Duran Duran
   c. The Grinch

14. What does Olaf call the giant snow creature that Elsa magics up?
   a. Snowy McSnowface
   b. Marshmallow
   c. Johnny Marr

15. What does Pabbie say is the only thing that can melt a frozen heart?
   a. Sensible amounts of warm water
   b. True love
   c. Lemsip and a walk

16. What knocks Elsa unconscious?
   a. Shards of an ice chandelier
   b. Too much prosecco
   c. A boulder called Phillip Stoneman

17. What happens when Hans's sword swings at Anna by accident?
    a. It shatters on her frozen form, into many pieces
    b. Anna starts singing that song again
    c. Time starts to flow backwards

18. But Anna is not dead – why?
    a. Her sacrifice to save her sister was one of true love so the curse is lifted
    b. She was only joking
    c. Elsa had built an ice version of Anna as a distraction

19. What does Elsa give to Olaf so he can enjoy the summer?
    a. A set of speedos and awesome shades
    b. Two hundred pounds and a ticket to Malta
    c. His own cloud, to keep him from melting in the heat

20. Who is the new ruler of the ice castle?
    a. Mr. Castle the castle-ruling king of Castilla
    b. Marshmallow – he survived and found Elsa's tiara
    c. Nobody – it's a fundamentally undemocratic position

Answers on page 274

Gremlins

This 1984 gross-out horror/comedy also provides a commentary on the commercialisation of Christmas, as well as a large message about the decadence of the season in the West. But we don't care about that so much, do we? We love the little critters, and we really love to watch the chaos unfold... So set off the madness with this set of questions about the legendary movie.

20 Questions

1. Where does Randall go to try and find a present for his son, Billy?
   a. An antiques-type store in Chinatown
   b. A supermarket in New Jersey
   c. The biggest Target in North America

2. And what is Randall's main occupation?
   a. Lawyer
   b. Inventor
   c. Rally Driver

3. He is enchanted by the Mogwai. But it is not for sale. How does he eventually buy it?
   a. He steals it by distracting Mr. Wing with a special firework he's invented
   b. Mr. Wing's grandson secretly sells it to him
   c. The Mogwai jumps into Randall's pocket when he is not looking

4. What are the three golden rules of Mogwai ownership?
   a. Do not let them watch TV; Do not let them stroke dogs; Do not let them eat crisps
   b. Two walks per day; Eat only sugar; Never wake a sleeping Mogwai
   c. Sunlight will kill them; Do not let them near water; Do not feed them after midnight

5. Where does Billy work?
    a. A bank
    b. Nuclear power plant
    c. A vet

6. What happens when Billy's friend Pete spills water on Gizmo the Mogwai?
    a. He grows wings
    b. It burns him
    c. Five more Mogwai are born from that spot

7. How do the new Mogwai trick Billy into feeding them after midnight?
    a. They turn all the clocks back one hour
    b. They cut the cord on Billy's alarm clock
    c. They tell him that it is always midnight somewhere in the world, so the rule doesn't make sense

8. What happens to the creatures as a result?
    a. They form cocoons, from which nasty little reptile-like critters hatch
    b. They grow enormous beer guts and fart loudly and stinkily
    c. They die

9. Who is the first human victim of the Gremlins?
   a. Mrs. Hatch
   b. Mr. Blobby
   c. Mr. Hanson

10. Billy and his mum Lynn manage to see off most of the Gremlins in various gruesome and gnarly ways – but who escapes?
   a. Gizmo
   b. Chewie
   c. Stripe

11. And where does that Gremlin head for, with dramatic results?
   a. Santa's Grotto, where he eats all the elves
   b. The swimming pool at a local YMCA
   c. A strip club, where he gets a new job

12. Why does Billy's girlfriend Kate hate Christmas?
   a. Her father broke his neck coming down a chimney, dressed as Santa
   b. Her mother told her Santa Claus wasn't real
   c. She gave her boyfriend George her heart, but the next day he gave it away

13. What movie are the Gremlins enjoying in the local cinema?
    a. *Critters*
    b. *Raiders of the Lost Ark*
    c. *Snow White and the Seven Dwarfs*

14. And how do Billy and Kate see off the majority of the Gremlins there?
    a. A gas explosion
    b. Electrocuting the cinema seats
    c. Poisoned sweets

15. How does Gizmo finally get the better of Stripe?
    a. Judo mastery that ties Stripe in a knot
    b. Asking him *Would You Rather*? questions that flummox him
    c. Opening a skylight, letting sun in and killing him

16. Gizmo is taken home by Mr. Wing in the end. But what does the Mogwai do?
    a. Sings a Christmas song
    b. Speaks and says: ‘Bye, Billy’
    c. Asks Mr. Wing for a bag of sweets

17. Which legendary animator makes a cameo in the bar?
    a. Walt Disney
    b. Seth McFarlane
    c. Chuck Jones

18. When Stripe hides in the cuddly toys, which alien from another movie can we also see?
    a. Alf, Alien Life Form
    b. E.T. the Extra Terrestrial
    c. Barney the Dinosaur

19. Blink and you'll miss it – but in the convention centre, a certain famous director zooms past in an electric wheelchair. Who is it?
    a. George Lucas
    b. Muir Matheison
    c. Steven Spielberg

20. What is the name of the sequel to *Gremlins*?
    a. *Gremlins 2: The New Batch*
    b. *Gremlins Schemlins: Hannukah Hell*
    c. *The Return of Mr. Wing: This Time it's War*

Bonus question: *Gremlins*, along with *Indiana Jones and the Temple of Doom*, had a lasting impact on something fundamental about the movie industry. But what was it?

Answers on page 274

The Grinch

First it was a popular book by one of the most inventive, rhyme-tastic authors out there, and then it became not one but two successful movies. Here's a bundle of questions about the whole kaboodle, which we trust will stop any sense of Grinchiness before it begins. Then again...

Bah Humbug

Who is the biggest Grinch around the table/in the house/ at the party? You must provide a convincing argument as to how they qualify for this dubious accolade.
Bonus point: Make up a four-line rhyming verse about them.

20 Questions

1. Easy-peasy: Who wrote the original book on which the movie was based?
2. Not so easy-peasy: What is that author's real name?

The 2000 Movie

3. What is the full title of the 2000 live action movie?
4. And who is the star performer in that one?
5. Can you name the famous narrator?
6. What is the name of the town in which the action is set?
7. What was wrong with the Grinch's heart?
8. What is the name of the Grinch's dog?
9. How many years has the Grinch spent living alone?

The 2018 Animated Movie

10. In the 2018 animated movie, what is the name of the Grinch's reindeer?

11. At the tree-lighting ceremony, where does the Grinch see in a flashback?

12. Who does the Grinch disguise himself as on Christmas Eve?

13. Which song do the Whos sing even though they have no gifts on Christmas Day?

14. And what happens to the Grinch when he hears it?

15. Who surprisingly returns to help the Grinch save the presents?

16. Finally, in this version who plays the Grinch?

About the book author. These are tough!

17. If you got number one right – congratulations! But can you guess how many copies of their books have been sold over the years? (Clue: It's a *lot*!)

18. How many different words are used, in total, in *The Cat in the Hat*?

19. How do you pronounce the author's surname? (Be careful!)

20. Very tricky, this: which other pen-names did the author use in his lifetime?

Answers on page 275

Harry Potter

It is estimated (by us, just now) that at any given moment in the universe someone is reading, watching, or pretending to be Harry Potter. None more so of course than at Chrimbo, when you're very likely to come across one whilst flicking through the channels. Beware – once you get sucked in to watching one of these movies it's very unlikely indeed you'll stop at just that. The series proper is a time-sink unparalleled in this dimension and that's before we even get on to the prequels… maybe a few questions might be a quicker way to get to the heart of the matter?

20 Questions

1. What is the first name of the person that wrote the original books?
2. And their middle name?
3. How many movies are there in the series (not including the prequels)?
4. A point for each – name them!
5. Easy one, this: which actor plays Harry?
6. And who plays Hermione?
7. And Ron?
8. What is the name of the major baddie in the movies?
9. What is the name of the major sport in the movies?
10. How old is Harry in the first movie?
11. What special powers does the Philosopher's Stone have?
12. Two different actors played Albus Dumbledore. Who were they?
13. In the *Fantastic Beasts* prequels, who played a younger Dumbledore?
14. What is the name of the Potterworld MMORPG that was launched in 2023?

15. Inevitably, in 2011 there was a TV Movie about the author, made unofficially by the Lifetime TV Channel in Canada. Do you know the name of it?
16. And what was Rowling's reaction?
17. Back to the movies and books now. What is the name for the non-magical people?
18. What is the name of the fragments of a Dark wizard's soul that can confer immortality?
19. And what is the only way to create one?
20. And what is the revelation of where a crucial one is?

Answers on page 276

The Holiday

On paper, going on holiday is wonderful. In real life, it's a series of frustrating queuing and expensive breakfasts before having to come home to the freezing cold and drizzly grey trudge of modern life. Still, the memories last forever, don't they? All except the good ones, anyway.

Challenge

Set a timer for 30 seconds. Name as many songs featuring words associated with holidays as you can, including the singer/artist. Multiple player game is possible; rather than shouting the names out loud, everyone gets a pen and paper and writes them down. Highest number of accurate titles and musicians wins – with variations in spelling allowed at the discretion of the quizmeister.

This Has No Point

You will need: paper and pencils; a timer; the lyrics to (for example) Madonna's 'Holiday' (seen only by the quizmeister).

How to play: Everyone except one player has one minute to write down any word in the Madonna hit 'Holiday' that has over four letters in it. The single player, without seeing any of their answers, then has to also write down **three** words of four letters or over. The the quizmeister reveals a) whether each answer, in turn, is correct when compared to the 'Holiday' lyrics; and b) how many of the other players have written the same word down. If the player has written a word that is in the song, **and** none of the others have thought of it, the player wins. If either the word is incorrect, or someone else has thought of it, the player has not won this time.

Variation: Each player has a song each to work from.

Variation 2: Each player writes down only three words (so are *all* playing). If a player has a word that nobody else has thought of, and is in the song, then they win that round. If two or more players have won a round, they go through to a knockout round based on a different song; if there are still two or more players they play another round with another song; keep going until there is only one winner.

(We really don't know how we come up with these definitely original ideas, ya know. Incidentally, we're writing a cosy crime novel about a gang of people that meet on a specific day to form a kind of collective to investigate murders. Agents, contact us to the usual address.)

20 Questions

1. What is Iris Simpkins' job?
    a. Weatherperson
    b. Society columnist
    c. Juggler

2. And what is Amanda Woods' job?
    a. Movie trailer producer
    b. Examinations provider
    c. Daredevil

3. What do the two women have in common, romance-wise?

   a. Both their partners cheated on them
   b. They always go for much taller men
   c. They are both considering going on Tinder

4. Which legendary actor plays Arthur, Amanda's neighbour?

   a. Clint Eastwood
   b. Miguel Almiron
   c. Eli Wallach

5. And which legendary actor has an uncredited cameo in the video store?

   a. Dustin Hoffman
   b. David Hasselhoff
   c. Hoffmeister the Bear

6. What is the name of the beautiful cottage in the country?

   a. Rainhill Station
   b. Rosehill Cottage
   c. Rastafarian Collage

7. What is unusual about the building?
   a. It has three bathrooms, but only one bedroom
   b. It doesn't exist in real life, having been built as a set only
   c. It is an early example of neo-Brutalist architecture

8. What relation is Graham to Iris?
   a. Cousin
   b. Father
   c. Brother

9. And how does Miles know Amanda?
   a. He is the composer of music for her movie trailers
   b. He is Jack Black, so very well-known in general
   c. He is the President of the United States of America

10. Another cameo question: which two actors appear in the trailer for *Deception* that we briefly see?
   a. Lindsay Lohan and James Franco
   b. Cat Stevens and Charlie Brooker
   c. Larry Grayson and Les Dawson

11. What does Iris persuade Arthur to do?
   a. Take up golf again
   b. Speak at a Writers' Guild event
   c. Ride a Harley-Davidson motorbike

12. What has Amanda not done since her parents divorced?
    a. Ridden a Harley-Davidson motorbike
    b. Cried
    c. Washed her underpants

13. How many daughters does Graham have?
    a. 6
    b. 2
    c. 1

14. Who turns up out of the blue to see Iris?
    a. Jasper, her old boyfriend
    b. Casper, the friendly ghost
    c. Rasta, the rastafarian

15. But what is Iris's reaction?
    a. She tells him to go away
    b. She screams in terror
    c. She doesn't answer the door

16. What triumph does Arthur achieve at the gala?
    a. He wins seven Academy Awards
    b. He meets his old friend, Arch Stanton
    c. He walks onto the stage without any help

17. And what happens between Miles and Iris?
    a. They both start to eat the same piece of spaghetti from different sides
    b. Miles asks her out, she says yes, and they kiss
    c. Miles asks Jasper out, he says yes, and they kiss

18. What does Amanda say to the lovestruck Graham when she is about to leave?
    a. That she is married to a man called John Doolittle
    b. That she is prepared to give their relationship a go, long-distance
    c. That she has no intention of ever seeing him again

19. But what really happens?
    a. Amanda can't bring herself to leave, and returns to the cottage
    b. Amanda falls for the taxi driver and makes a new life in Surrey
    c. Amanda breaks her leg running for an airport bus, and has to go to hospital

20. Quote time: Who does Arthur say he likes because 'he cuts a nice suit'?
    a. Man At C&A
    b. Man At B&Q
    c. Hugo Boss

Answers on page 278

Home Alone

Who lives in a house like this? As it turns out, so many people that one gets left behind by accident. Oopsie! Still, without that particular piece of plot the movie would be a whole lot shorter and basically just a static camera filming someone's empty family home, so...

A Family Affair

Discuss: if you had to leave one of your family/friend group at home alone to fend off some baddies, who would be your choice – and why would they be best suited to this role?

Never Have I Ever

A point for each. Up to you to decide if the highest scorer wins… or loses!

- ★ Called someone a filthy animal (yes, we know that's in the sequel, so please don't write in)
- ★ Thrown away an important document/ticket by mistake
- ★ Overslept and had to dash to school/work/holiday
- ★ Left a tap running by accident, causing a small flood
- ★ Taken a flight/train/bus to a destination miles from where you need to be
- ★ Watched a church choir
- ★ Set up a bunch of booby traps in your house
- ★ Been in a treehouse
- ★ Slipped on some ice
- ★ Handled a tarantula (or other big spider)

20 Questions

1. Easy one to start you off: on which day does the main action take place?
    a. Halloween
    b. Boxing Day
    c. Christmas Eve

2. What is the real-life location of the house in the movie?
    a. A village outside Chicago, Illinois
    b. A village outside Toronto, Ontario
    c. A village outside Moonbase Alpha, Luna

3. To which European destination did the McCallister family – sans Kevin – go on holiday?
    a. Berlin, Germany
    b. Paris, France
    c. Llanfairpwllgwyngyllgogerechwyndrobwy-lllantisiliogogogoch, Wales

4. Extra point bonus question: say answer 3c out loud. You may read from this book – but for two bonus points do it without looking!

5. How old is Kevin in the movie?
    a. 8
    b. 9
    c. 42

6. Why can't the family get in touch with Kevin from France?
   a. Paris has an incompatible phone system
   b. Chicago's phone lines are all down
   c. Their mobile battery is flat

7. To where does Kate manage to get a flight?
   a. Arch Stanton
   b. Scranton
   c. Shelbyville

8. What kind of band is Gus Polinski leader of?
   a. Punk rock
   b. Salsa
   c. Polka

9. And who is the actor that portrays Gus?
   a. John Goodman
   b. John McEnroe
   c. John Candy

10. Famously, that actor did all his scenes in one day, as a favour to his friend, screenwriter and producer John Hughes. But do you know how much that actor was paid?
   a. $1 million
   b. $414
   c. Six crocodiles

11. The weather doesn't always behave how filmmakers want it to. So what did the production use in lieu of snow outside the McCallister house near the end?

   a. Dry ice
   b. Polystyrene
   c. Mashed potato flakes

12. Which actor, more famous for mobster movies, played Harry the thief?

   a. Robert de Niro
   b. James Gandolfini
   c. Joe Pesci

13. Why is Kevin scared of Old Man Marley?

   a. The rumours are that Marley killed all his own family
   b. Marley was said to possess special evil powers
   c. People believed that Marley was The Grinch

14. In the airport scene, where Kate is having trouble at the desk, which megastar is rumoured to be visible in the background?

   a. Michael Jackson
   b. Johnny Rotten
   c. Elvis Presley

15. What is the name of the actor who portrays Kevin's cousin, Fuller?
   a. Kieran Culkin
   b. Christopher Columbus
   c. Kaptain Krunch

16. What does Kevin use to heat up the doorknob?
   a. A box of matches
   b. A BBQ grill lighter
   c. Fireworks

17. What is the meal that Kevin never gets to finish because he's defending the house from the burglars?
   a. Hot dog
   b. Pumpkin pie
   c. Mac and cheese

18. What is the name of the black-and-white film that Kevin watches, whilst eating a massive bowl of ice-cream, and then uses to fool the thieves?
   a. *Filthy Animals*
   b. *Angels With Filthy Souls*
   c. *The Devil Went Down To Memphis*

19. What implement does Marley use to bash Harry and Marv?

    a. A rake
    b. A trowel
    c. A shovel

20. How many Academy Awards (Oscars) was *Home Alone* nominated for?

    a. 0
    b. 2
    c. 6

Answers on page 278

It's a Wonderful Life

The one that began it all; a beautifully-shot, deftly-realised take on the Dickens classic which we won't name cause it's one of the questions and we've already given the answer away. Still, luckily nobody really takes any notice of these bits so we reckon we're safe...

Challenge: Name five wonderful things in your life.
Twist: Name five things that would make your life even more wonderful.
Double Twist: Try and name five ways you could make someone else's life more wonderful.

Through the Looking Glass

How would the world be different if these things never existed? And what creative ways might people use to make up for their absences?

- ★ sprouts
- ★ movies
- ★ mobile phones
- ★ football
- ★ guitars
- ★ bridges
- ★ dogs
- ★ trees
- ★ money
- ★ sweets
- ★ school
- ★ aeroplanes
- ★ Christmas

Would You Rather

Would you rather see how the world would be without you, or see how the world would be with two of you?

Would you rather be able to talk with angels, or be able to fly whenever you wanted?
Would you rather be a 1940s movie star, or write music for 1940s movies?

Weepies

It's a Wonderful Life is one of the most emotionally-affecting movies out there at Christmas, with everything from despair and defeat to triumph and redemption. Which one of your friends/family is the most likely to shed a tear at this (or any other) movie, and why? Which movie is the most unlikely one at which someone has shed a tear in your group? Be honest – it could be you! And there's nothing wrong with that, of course! It's a natural and lovely human response to art.

20 Questions

1. Easy-peasy starter: what is the name of the main character?

2. And the name of the famous actor playing that character?

3. Trickier: can you name the short story that it was based on?

4. Trickier still: and which famous Christmas-themed redemption story was *that* one loosely based on?

5. What drastic and final act is the main character contemplating as we join them?
6. Who stops him doing so?
7. We enter flashback territory now. How does George become deaf in his left ear?
8. And how does he intervene at the pharmacy?
9. Why does George have to postpone his planned travels?
10. Why does Harry not take over from George?
11. What does Uncle Billy accidentally do which wrecks everything?
12. What is Henry Potter's response when George asks for a loan, based on George's life assurance?
13. We turn to the alternative world without George now. What is the new name of the town?
14. Where is the pharmacist in this version of the world?
15. And what becomes of Harry?
16. What does Mary do when George finds her in this alternate universe?
17. The alternative world is deleted when George realises he is valuable. But there is still money to find. What happens now?

18. What is the name of the book that Clarence has gifted to George?
19. And what is the inscription?
20. How does George know that Clarence has also succeeded in his angelic quest?

Answers on page 279

Jack Frost

Let's get it absolutely clear: we are talking about the 1998 movie, and not the film of the same title that came out a year previously. That one stars Scott MacDonald, is directed by Michael Cooney, and is what you might call a slasher/horror, which has become a direct-to-TV cult 'classic'. No judgement here of course; we're rather chuffed to find out that there was even a 2000 sequel called, brilliantly, Jack Frost 2: Revenge of the Mutant Killer Snowman. *Marvellous. Back to more family-friendly territory we go, though, with a clutch of questions to get you tingling from your head to your tippy toes.*

20 Questions

1. In which fictional town is the movie set?
   a. Springfield, Dakota
   b. Medford, Colorado
   c. South Park, Colorado

2. What 'magical' object does Jack give Charlie?
   a. A harmonica
   b. A harp
   c. A half-penny

3. What event does Jack miss, in favour of recording a song?
   a. Charlie's hockey game
   b. Christmas party
   c. Charlie's birthday

4. Jack borrows his bandmate's car to go to the mountains, but what instrument does that bandmate play?
   a. Bass guitar
   b. Keyboards
   c. Spoons

5. But what happens?
   a. Jack crashes the car in a snowstorm and dies
   b. Jack takes a wrong turn and ends up in Los Angeles
   c. Jack cannot drive, so the movie stops

6. A year passes; what is Charlie doing when he gets very emotional?
   a. Shovelling snow
   b. Eating cheese
   c. Playing *Red Dead Redemption*

7. What does Charlie build, to remember his dad?
   a. A studio
   b. A wall on the Mexican border
   c. A snowman

8. And what happens when Charlie plays the harmonica?
   a. The snowman comes alive
   b. The snowman flies in the air
   c. It is a high-pitched harmonica that only dogs can hear, so Charlie becomes King of the Hounds

9. How does the snowman convince Charlie that he is actually Jack?
    a. He buys him his favourite KFC
    b. He calls him 'Charlie Boy'
    c. He tells him that Santa is real

10. What does Jack convince Charlie to re-join?
    a. His hockey team
    b. The church
    c. The joinery club at school

11. Why is it difficult for Jack to get to Charlie's hockey game?
    a. He can't drive as his hands keep slipping off the wheel
    b. He is starting to melt
    c. He is frozen solid

12. Where does Charlie think would be the best place for Jack to go?
    a. The cabin in the mountains, because it is cold up there
    b. Jamaica, because he can melt into the sea and always be happy
    c. In the freezer at their local restaurant, so he can eat all the fish

13. When Gabby arrives at the cabin, what happens?
    a. Jack appears in a mirror, saying hi to her
    b. All the snowman garb is gone, so they see Jack as a happier spirit
    c. Charlie is taken to hospital for treatment as he has eaten hallucinogenic reindeer poop

14. And where does Jack go?
    a. To heaven
    b. To Philadelphia
    c. To Madison Square Garden

15. Who is the actor playing Jack?
    a. Michael Crawford
    b. Buster Keaton
    c. Michael Keaton

16. And who plays Gabby, Charlie's mum?
    a. Kelly Preston
    b. Robert Peston
    c. Jasper Conran

17. Tougher one, this: which actor plays Charlie?
    a. Mark Wahlberg
    b. Charles Iceberg
    c. Joseph Cross

18. Three kids of a famous musician appear in the movie. What's their surname?

   a. Jackson
   b. Beatles
   c. Zappa

19. What is the name of the school bully who later forms a bond with Charlie over their mutual lack of a dad?

   a. Gripper Stebson
   b. Agamemnon Tailpipe
   c. Rory Buck

20. Who would win in a fight between The Snowman, from *The Snowman*, and the snowman from *Jack Frost*?

   a. The Snowman
   b. Jack Frost
   c. It would end in a draw

Answers on page 280

James Bond

Christmas wouldn't be Christmas without a Bond movie or ten on the telly, would it? It's traditional that Bond be jumping off cliffs, fighting baddies and drinking Martinis on the screen, whilst random satiated uncles and aunts doze on the sofa, dribbling and snoring and generally making you wonder at the wide range of human possibilities.

Challenges

Name as many Bond movies as you can. There's a lot more than you think!

Sing as many Bond themes as you can.

Act out scenes from a Bond movie of your choice.

Play *James Bond* charades.

Spend an hour talking like a spy.

Who would make the best spy that you know? Why?

Over To You

Create a spy movie plot of your own. Here's some ideas that might help:

Who's the lead character?
Which actor plays them?
Who is their love interest?
Who's the baddie?
Where is it set?
What's the big twist?
What cool gadgets does your hero have?
And which ones does the baddie have?

10 Silly Questions

1. What was Sean Connery's favourite sport and at what time did he like to play it?
2. What do you call an aquatic spy?
3. Which *James Bond* actor has a name that seems to indicate he would like additional sexytime?
4. Beth dach chi'n galw actor sy'n hoffi ddringo fynyddoedd?
5. What do you call a vegan movie producer who's put on a few pounds over Christmas?
6. Why could James Bond sleep through the earthquake?
7. Why did Bond have to wait ages for a new gun from Giants R Us?
8. What rapper does James Bond's boss turn into when she looks into a mirror?
9. Why do cats hate Bond?
10. Which Bond villain is also a shark?

And 10 Sensible Ones

1. Who is the original writer of the *Bond* novels?
2. For a point each, name any other writers of the full-length Bond books.

3. And who is the author of the series of *Young Bond* novels?
4. What was the name of the trilogy of novels in the mid-late noughties written by Kate Westbrook?
5. And what is that author's real name?
6. When is Bond's birthday?
7. Which actor returned to the role for 1983's *Never Say Never Again*?
8. Which three Bond movies have gold in their titles?
9. Who is the youngest person to have written, recorded and performed an official Bond movie theme?
10. And which three Bond themes did Welsh belter Shirley Bassey sing?

Answers on page 281

Jingle All the Way

Lots of running around in this one with scene upon scene of the characters chasing things, narrowly missing things, and generally being a little bit too late to do what they were supposed to do. It's exhausting to watch, to be honest, but then isn't that what Christmas is all about? Being far too tired and washed out by the pressure and the preparations to really enjoy any of it?

Round Round Round Round I Get Around

Gather together your people and sing 'Jingle Bells' as a round, including the verses.

The way to do this is that the first person starts singing the song alone for the first line, then as soon as they start singing line two, another person starts from the first line, singing at the same time. Keep singing 'til you reach the end – and you can even start again if you feel specially inspired.

This particular Christmas carol works very well as a round – you can keep adding people for as long as you like, and it should still sound really good. Including the verses!

If you are a Makaton/BSL/ASL or any other sign language speaker – signing the lyrics is absolutely a lot of fun :) Use as much slang as you like – see who breaks the round first!

And, if someone is convinced they really cannot sing – they can mime the actions of the lyrics. No escaping this one.

Forfeit: If someone forgets their words/comes in at the wrong time/trips up… they have to begin the whole song again, and everyone else joins in again as above.

20 Questions

1. What is the name of the toy that is in huge demand in the movie?

2. Where is the movie set?
3. What event does Howard miss that he is trying to make up for?
4. Why has he left it so late?
5. What is the name of Harold's rival who also has the same idea?
6. Where does Howard think he will find a version of the toy?
7. But what happens?
8. How does Howard get out of trouble?
9. What is the name of the event that Jamie wants Howard to promise to attend?
10. Myron says that his own dad didn't get him a particular toy for Christmas. What was it?
11. Whoa! Myron and Howard have a chance to get the toy they're looking for. How do they find out that one is available?
12. But what are they told is actually available?
13. How do the pair escape this time?
14. Why can't Howard drive his car home?
15. Desperate for the toy, what does Howard plan to do now?

16. He doesn't go through with it – but gets caught anyway. Who takes his family to the Xmas event instead?
17. That person does not cover themselves in glory either. How so?
18. Why is Howard having to hide in a store cupboard?
19. It works out for him – seemingly – but Myron is also there. Describe the scene!
20. At the very, very (post-credits) end, what does Liz ask Howard that sends him into another worry?

Answers on page 283

Klaus

Oh, we all love a good origin story, don't we? Well, we aren't going to give out too many spoilers for this one. Suffice it to say that as Klaus develops, lots of different things happen in terms of attitude, attire, mode of transport and yearly tasks. These, taken together, all add up to a character that we all know, love, and secretly still believe in. But enough about Eric Morecambe, here's some testing questions...

20 Questions

1. Which item do we follow at the start of the movie?
   a. A letter
   b. A Christmas present
   c. A cat

2. Who is summoned to see the drill sergeant?
   a. Jake Bugg
   b. Jesper Johansen
   c. Scarlett Johannson

3. What is the name of the town where Jesper's dad sends him to work?
   a. Belieberville
   b. Cowabunga City
   c. Smeerensburg

4. And how many letters must Jesper deliver in a year?
   a. 500
   b. 6,000
   c. 100,000

5. Or what will happen?
   a. Jesper will have to use email instead
   b. The secret goat people will form an army
   c. Jesper will be cut off from his family

6. When Jesper is tricked into ringing the bell, what happens?
   a. A massive fight breaks out between two rival clans
   b. A rock-and-roll gig starts, with the loudest guitarist being crowned king
   c. Nothing – the bell is only there for tourists to take pictures of

7. How many letters does Jesper deliver on his first day?
   a. 100
   b. 80085
   c. 0

8. What does Jesper find in the woodsman Mr. Klaus's house?
   a. Hundreds of unposted letters to Santa
   b. A treasure trove of beautiful hand-made toys
   c. A Big Bad Wolf lying in bed

9. What falls out of Jesper's satchel as he runs away from the returning Mr. Klaus?
   a. A drawing made by a young lad
   b. A book called *Santa Is Bigger Than The Beatles*
   c. Seven hundred dollars in non-consecutive banknotes

10. And what does Mr. Klaus want Jesper to do as a result?

   a. Get gone, and stay gone. He just lost his Smeerensburg privileges
   b. Go to the boy's house with him so Jesper can deliver a package from Klaus
   c. Read him excerpts of the time that Santa went to visit Elvis

11. As a result of making that delivery, what does Jesper wake up to see?

   a. He has been transformed overnight into a giant insect
   b. It has snowed so much that everything is like a giant marshmallow
   c. A line of kids outside his house, waiting for him so they can mail letters to Klaus

12. Why are the boy and the girl not allowed to play together?

   a. They are from opposing clans
   b. They have got the rules wrong
   c. They should be in school

13. Why does Jesper say that the boy got coal instead of a present?
    a. Because Mr. Klaus wanted the boy to make a nice warm fire
    b. Because Mr. Klaus rewards good people and gives coal to naughty ones
    c. Because Mr. Klaus was sick and tired of people bothering him

14. Why does Mr. Klaus's wagon losing its wheels make people think he's special?
    a. Because when the reindeer and the wagon go over a big hill, it looks like they can fly
    b. Because the wheels were made out of delicious chocolate over marshmallow, and a biscuity centre
    c. Because Mr. Klaus predicted that one day he would drive a wheel-less wagon

15. What item does Jesper try and make for Margu?
    a. A sled with a sail
    b. A shed with a nail
    c. Some sild with a little tail

16. Why did Mr. Klaus keep making birdhouses?
   a. He wanted to put a little one in your soul
   b. In tribute to his late wife, Lydia, who loved birds
   c. To trap special Yumbirds he could roast for lunch

17. What do the clans plan to do, to start the villagers fighting again?
   a. Destroy all the presents
   b. Pay people £200 to punch each other
   c. Put on a play called *Fighty Fight Good Good*

18. The presents fall out of the sleigh – disaster! But it's *not* a disaster – why?
   a. The presents were always a metaphor for the sharing of love over the Christmas season
   b. Mr. Klaus casts a spell, and they all float gently to the ground, singing beautifully
   c. All those 'presents' were actually just logs – the real ones are safe in the workshop

19. Why do Mr. Krum and Mrs. Ellingboe – the clan leaders – have to get on with each other at the end?
   a. They have fallen in love with each other
   b. They both have shares in Mr. Klaus Toymakers, Incorporated
   c. Their kids, Pumpkin and Olaf, have gotten married

20. How many kids do Jesper and Alva have at the end?
    a. 2
    b. 6
    c. 6,000

Answers on page 285

Krampus

Who doesn't love a delicious bit of horror-comedy now and again? Well, if you don't then Krampus *really isn't the movie for you. Worry not, it's technically a PG-13, though it is still spooky and dark enough to leave an imprint on the unsuspecting viewer. For some, of course, there can be no finer a recommendation.*

Disclaimer duly given, let's see how much of an impact this slab of gnarly seasonal fun really has had on you...

20 Questions

1. Which song is playing during the opening montage, where everyone's going absolutely crazy doing their Christmas shopping?
    a. 'Santa Baby'
    b. 'Krampus Baby'
    c. 'It's Beginning to Look a Lot Like Christmas'

2. Tom and Sarah Engel have to intercede in a fight between their son Max and another kid. But what sparked the brawl?
    a. The other kid dissed Santa
    b. The other kid said Max was The Grinch
    c. Max was bullying the kid for his new Air Max shoes, which he said he owned

3. Max's grandmother is from Germany. How do the family address her?
    a. Apfelkopf
    b. Omi
    c. Omnibussen

4. What do Max's cousins do that causes him to flip out again?
   a. Throw his X-Box out of the window
   b. Read his diary, and reveal he has a secret crush
   c. Read his letter to Santa and take the mickey out of him for believing in Father Christmas

5. Why does Max's sister, Beth, go out in the snowstorm?
   a. To get some more bread and jam as the oven is not working
   b. To see if Santa has arrived with their presents
   c. To check on her boyfriend after a power cut

6. What do Tom and Howard find in said boyfriend's house?
   a. It has been trashed completely, and there are hoofprints resembling a goat's
   b. It is festooned in so many Christmas lights that it has led to a massive power surge
   c. It is actually an interstellar spaceship from which aliens have landed

7. How does the fire start in the Engels' house?
    a. A log from the fire rolls into the tree and sets it plus the presents on fire
    b. Working-class revolutionaries, having read Max's theories, begin to revolt
    c. An alien spaceship zaps it with a cool laser gun from space

8. Who does Omi reveal is actually chasing them?
    a. Krampus
    b. Grampus Eight
    c. Pumpernickel Justice, FBI

9. Why is this happening?
    a. For stealing bread from the duck pond
    b. Because they have not sung the correct words to 'Edelweiss'
    c. For losing the Spirit of Christmas

10. What happened in the past to Omi's community?
    a. They organised into strong unions and seized the means of production
    b. Krampus took them all into hell, apart from Omi
    c. Krampus ate them but didn't enjoy it as they gave him indigestion

11. What did Krampus leave behind that time?
   a. One of his claws
   b. A bauble with his name on it
   c. A magical whistle

12. Who do the family find trying to eat Jordan?
   a. A malevolent tree sprite called Bolax
   b. A lion with eight legs and six hundred eyes
   c. A jack-in-a-box called Der Klown

13. What is the fate of Dorothy and Chrissie at this point?
   a. They fight the lion and become demigods
   b. They break all the windows, letting in the snowstorm
   c. A bunch of elves under the aegis of Krampus kidnap them

14. Where does the family try and hide?
   a. Inside a snowplough
   b. Up the chimney
   c. Philadelphia

15. But what happens?
    a. They are eaten by the Snow Monster
    b. They have lost the keys so freeze to death
    c. Nothing much. Time passes. Everyone gets a bit older and more wrinkled

16. After fighting Omi, what does Krampus do?
    a. Goes to find somewhere quiet for a nice lie down
    b. Turns on the television to watch *Gremlins*
    c. Gives Max a bauble – wrapped up in Max's Santa letter

17. What does Max do?
    a. Chases Krampus and apologises for losing his Spirit of Christmas
    b. Chases Krampus and bonks him on the clonk like a gonk
    c. Tells Krampus to grow up and stop being a dumb-bum

18. What does Krampus do?
    a. Throws Max and Stevie into hell anyway
    b. Apologises and promises to change his ways
    c. Buys everyone a massive turkey from a shop that is open somehow on Christmas Day

19. Max wakes up the next day in bed. All a dream! But how do we know it probably wasn't so?
    a. *Krampus* is being shown on television, on every channel
    b. The bauble is in one of Max's presents, and everyone starts to recall the previous night
    c. Krampus and Max perform a dance routine with a soft-shoe shuffle, and sing about the movie

20. Where is, in fact, the house now?
    a. In the Land of Make Believe exhibition at the World's Fair
    b. In space, as it is a spaceship from the Gravalax Frink cluster
    c. In a snow globe in hell – as are many, many others that Krampus is looking after

Answers on page 285

Last Christmas

Sometimes you just gotta roll with it and indulge yourself in a rom-com-ghost-musical don't you? Well, good news – Last Christmas *hits all the buttons to make you laugh, cry, cringe and sing along with some of the greatest pop songs ever written. Here are some questions to help you remember the plot, too.*

20 Questions

1. Which famous duo's song gives this movie its title?
   a. Big Fun
   b. Wham!
   c. Royal Blood

2. What is the day job of the aspiring singer, Kate?
   a. Elf
   b. Shrek
   c. Santa

3. What is Tom Webster doing when Kate first meets him?
   a. Running in circles
   b. Making soup
   c. Standing in the street looking upward

4. What happens when she does the same?
   a. She gets rained on
   b. A bird poos on her
   c. She falls over

5. Kate has to move back in with her family. Where are her parents originally from?
   a. Manchester
   b. Yugoslavia
   c. Latvia

6. Kate's dad, Ivan, is now working as a minicab driver. But what was his former job back home?

a. Dressmaker

b. Santa

c. Lawyer

7. Where does Kate begin helping, intending to run into Tom again?

a. At the supermarket

b. At a homeless shelter

c. At the school

8. That plot point's a bit like *Scrooged,* isn't it?

a. Yes

b. Yes

c. Yes

9. What secret of her sister Marta's does Kate blab to her parents?

a. That Marta is Santa

b. That Marta is gay

c. That Marta is a spy employed by Hugh Grant

10. After Kate storms off, she runs into Tom. Where do they go next?

   a. Tom's flat
   b. Tom's car
   c. Tom's tractor

11. What operation does Kate tell Tom she had the previous year?

   a. A leg transplant
   b. A heart transplant
   c. A pants transplant

12. What song do we hear when Kate busks to raise funds for the Shelter?

   a. 'Faith'
   b. 'Wake Me Up Before You Go-Go'
   c. 'Freedom'

13. Kate returns to Tom's apartment, only to find who there?

   a. Iron Maiden
   b. An estate agent
   c. A gang of mutant Gremlins

14. And what does she learn about the previous owner?
    a. That they were killed in a bicycle accident the previous Christmas
    b. That they were actually interplanetary visitors from the planet Zog
    c. That they were Andrew Ridgeley's long-lost cousin

15. And what does she realise about Tom?
    a. That he was the real Santa Claus
    b. That he was the heart donor that saved her life
    c. That he was born in a crossfire hurricane

16. And what about the bench where the two sat, on their first walk together?
    a. It was made of magic wood
    b. It was dedicated to Engelbert Humperdinck
    c. It was a memorial for Tom, who is actually a ghost

17. And which song does Kate inevitably sing at the Christmas Eve concert?
    a. 'Last Christmas'
    b. 'I Saw Mummy Kissing Santa Claus'
    c. 'You Suffer' by Napalm Death

18. Who joins Kate and her family for Christmas dinner?
   a. Tom, in a special robot shell
   b. Marta's girlfriend Alba
   c. Andrew Ridgeley

19. The action blends to the next summer. Where is Kate now?
   a. On holiday
   b. Sitting on the special bench
   c. Dancing in a production of *Rumpelstiltskin On Ice*

20. And what do we see her doing, as advised by Tom?
   a. Washing her face with a non-biological soap
   b. Looking up
   c. Looking for four-leaf clovers

Answers on page 286

Love Actually

Hey! That's a good idea for a movie quiz book title! Someone ought to publish one, so we can all have a good old argument around the Chrimbo dinner table! That sounds like an idea with literally no drawbacks whatsoever, doesn't it.

Knotting Actually

Make up a plot of a brand-new but certainly on-brand Hugh Grant movie. Here are a few suggestions for you to get your teeth into:

- ★ Who are the co-stars?
- ★ What job does Hugh do?
- ★ And why is he not considered a suitable match for his love interest at first?
- ★ What is the plot?
- ★ What is the big plot twist/surprise?
- ★ What does he have to do, to convince the girl/her family/her peers/his job that he is The One?
- ★ Which cheesy but hugely famous song features at the triumphant ending?
- ★ What compound of cursing would Hugh use throughout this one?

Your fellow players will give you marks for originality, aptness, and plausibility.
Bonus: Do an impression of Hugh Grant.
Double bonus: Ask a fellow player to interview you about the above movie, and in your answers do an impression of Grumpy Hugh at the 2023 Oscars.

25 Questions

1. Which screenwriter and producer wrote and directed the movie?

2. Which song is Billy Mack re-recording?
3. And what is the title of his new version?
4. Whose party does he miss to hang out with his manager Joe, instead?
5. Which song plays as Juliet and Peter come out of their wedding ceremony?
6. How does Mark finally show his love for Juliet?
7. What nationality is Aurélia?
8. And where does Jamie live?
9. What kind of company does Harry run?
10. And what role does Mia perform?
11. Which item does Karen find in Harry's pocket?
12. Instead of this item, what gift does she open on Christmas Day?
13. What relation is David to Karen?
14. And his job is?
15. The girl Sam has a crush on shares a name with whom?
16. And how does he tell her how he feels (note – there's no way this could happen today!)?
17. Where is Sarah's brother?

18. And what does Karl do when Michael phones?
19. What does the wedding caterer Colin think will bring him success in love?
20. And how many ladies does he somehow end up staying with?
21. How did John and Judy meet?
22. Which British production company/studio produced the movie?
23. Who was the only actor to win a British Academy Film Award (BAFTA) for their performance in the film?
24. In which category?
25. What was the name of the tongue-in-cheek short follow-up movie that was written for and aired by the charity Comic Relief for Red Nose Day, in 2017?

Answers on page 286

Miracle on 34th Street

Going Old-School on this one – all the questions below relate to the 1947 original movie, and not any modern remake. There's just something about that classic multiple-Oscar winning flick that we can't resist. So let's get stuck in to one of the most enduring Christmas films out there – how will you get on?

20 Questions

1. Did you know that this movie originally had a different UK title? What was it?
   - a. *Grandfather Thyme and His Grapes*
   - b. *Santa's Stolen My Boat*
   - c. *The Big Heart*

2. Why is Kris Kringle so annoyed about the Macy's Parade version of Santa?
   - a. Santa is drunk
   - b. Santa has odd socks
   - c. Santa is eating crisps

3. What does Doris Walker then convince Kris to do?
   - a. Join a circus
   - b. Take Santa's place
   - c. Go for a long walk off a short pier

4. Why is Susan unnerved by Santa?
   - a. She hears him speaking Dutch to a girl
   - b. She can see he has a false beard and bad breath
   - c. She thinks Santa is a pernicious capitalist construct

5. What does Susan ask Santa for as a present?
   a. Six hundred badgers in a special badger sanctuary for retired badgers
   b. A wonderful house, that she has seen in a magazine
   c. Simply that everyone is full of love and happiness

6. What does Granville Sawyer recommend happens to Kris?
   a. That he is sacked
   b. That he gets a bonus
   c. That he shaves his beard

7. And where does Kris Kringle end up next?
   a. In a psychiatric institution
   b. Philadelphia
   c. On an island near Cuba

8. What is the name of the judge in the hearing?
   a. Henry Q. Bandersnatch
   b. Happy D. Gilmore
   c. Henry X. Harper

9. And that of the District Attorney?
   a. Colonel Tom Parker
   b. Thomas Mara
   c. Mara O'Briain

10. What ruling does the attorney ask the judge to make?

a. That Santa is just a normal man. An innocent man
b. That Santa Claus does not exist
c. That Santa drinks Fanta with a Bantha for banter

11. Who is the witness that Fred Gailey calls, and who admits he believes Santa is real?

a. Edward Woodward
b. Chewbacca Motörhead
c. R. H. Macy

12. What does that witness do straight afterwards?

a. He fires Granville Sawyer
b. He kisses Granville Sawyer
c. He burns down the courtroom

13. Who else asserts that their dad told them Santa was real?

a. Thomas Mara's own son
b. Thomas Mara's daughter
c. Ken Dodd's dad's dog

14. What does Mara challenge Fred Gailey to do by the next day?
    a. Buy a way better suit, cause Fred looks like a big old mess
    b. Learn all the dance steps to the 'Macarena'
    c. Prove that Kris Kringle is the one and only Santa

15. Susan sends Kris a letter – which the New York Post Office sends to him. But what else do they send Kris?
    a. All the other letters that were addressed to Santa
    b. A 'we tried to deliver but you were out' card, even though he was literally waiting by the door
    c. All the biggest packages they can find, to cheer him up

16. What does Fred then do with all those bags?
    a. Burns them for winter fuel
    b. Puts them on the judge's desk to prove his point
    c. Makes a thousand paper aeroplanes

17. And the judge's response?
    a. Dismisses the case
    b. Sends Macy to jail
    c. Runs out of the courtroom screaming

18. What does Kris tell Susan at the Macy's party?
   a. That he is six hundred years old
   b. That Christmas is based on ancient pagan traditions
   c. That he couldn't get her that dream house

19. Kris drives them home via an unusual route – what does Doris see?
   a. That her own dream house is actually for sale
   b. A sleigh and reindeer parked by the chimney
   c. A ghost called Slimer coming straight for her

20. And Fred then suggests something to Doris – what is it?
   a. That they have a party involving seventy Santas
   b. That they get married and buy the house
   c. That there ought to be two more houses so they can all get one

Answers on page 287

The Muppet Christmas Carol

Not, as you might think, a version of A Christmas Carol *narrated by Danny Dyer, but the actual Jim Henson creations in one of the most entertaining and diverting takes on it you could hope for. And it features Hunter S. Thompson's favourite Muppet – Animal.*[1]

1 Yes we know Gonzo should be the punchline but we thought it was funnier this way, so there

Challenge Time

You will need:

- ★ A piece of paper each and coloured pencils/felt tips/crayons (depending what you have)
- ★ A timer or stopwatch
- ★ Your imagination

Game One

A New Muppet

One person is in charge of timing and suggestions.
In one minute, draw a new Muppet based on some, one, or all of these factors (set by the person in charge):

- ★ name
- ★ colour and type of fur
- ★ height and/or size
- ★ characteristic (for example, loves to tell jokes/is a pig/is green)
- ★ dreams and personality
- ★ anything else the quizmeister chooses!

After a minute, each player presents their new Muppet to the person in charge, who rates them out of ten points – highest mark wins.

Game Two

Fold-a-Muppet

Take a piece of paper and fold it into horizontal strips. This will make, for example, four 'creation zones'.

Each player takes it in turn to draw on the paper, making sure to only use their own area. For example, player one draws a new Muppet's head, then re-folds the paper so only the (blank) second creation zone is visible (and obscures their drawing). Then, the second player draws the arms and torso into creation zone two, afterwards folding the paper so creation zone three is visible. Player three then draws the legs, folding so zone four is free for the fourth player to draw the feet.

Only after everyone has drawn their zone can the full new Muppet be revealed in all its glory!

Variation: As above, but with two or more teams each creating a new Fold-A-Muppet of their own, with prompts given by a Muppetmeister as in *A New Muppet*.

Variation Two: Two players alternate creation zones on the same paper.

Variation Three: Two players each have their own paper but swap between creation zones, so try and complete each other's Muppet.

20 Questions

1. Which Muppet serves as the narrator (named Dickens) in the movie?
2. And who is his assistant?
3. Which megastar actor plays Ebenezer Scrooge?
4. And which Muppet is in the role of Bob Cratchit?
5. Which two Muppets come around, collecting money for charity?
6. But what is Ebenezer's harsh response?
7. Jacob Marley is one of Scrooge's former business partners, but what reggae-referencing name is given to Jacob's brother?
8. Which quick-to-criticise Muppet duo play the Marley roles?
9. What is the name of Scrooge's school sweetheart?
10. Who is Bob Cratchit's wife, as shown by the Ghost of Christmas Present?
11. The Ghost of Christmas Yet To Come shows Scrooge that Tiny Tim will not make it through to the next year. But which Muppet represents this tragic character?
12. What finally shocks Scrooge into changing his ways?

13. Who does he team up with to help with his Christmas feast?
14. And what does Scrooge say to Bob?
15. *The Muppet Christmas Carol* is of course a musical movie. Which character sings 'Chairman of the Board'?
16. And how about the band that gives us 'Fozziwig's Party'?
17. And which energetic Muppet is their drummer?
18. What is the name of Scrooge's song near the end?
19. What does Dickens reveal about Scrooge's new relationship to Tiny Tim?
20. And what becomes of Tiny Tim now?

Answers on page 288

National Lampoon's Christmas Vacation

Ah, the National Lampoon Vacation *series... the hapless family always seem to get into all kinds of japes and scrapes. Believe it or not, this 1989 movie is the third in a series of six – yes, six – all with roughly the same plot. Still, nobody's making anyone watch them, and they're a nice diversion and mostly extremely family friendly. So let's get into the spirit of Christmas and have a quick question session, with fingers crossed that it won't go off the rails/the theme park won't be closed/nobody will have their cameras nicked...*

20 Questions

1. An easy one: what's the surname of the family that stars in this, and the other movies?
2. Which comedy actor plays Clark, the dad of the family?
3. What's that actor's real name?
4. And who plays Ellen, his wife?
5. What have Audrey, Ellen and Rusty forgotten to bring to their tree-finding escapade?
6. Why is there a power cut across the city?
7. What breed of dog belongs to Catherine and Eddie?
8. And what is said dog's name?
9. Where are that family living, and why?
10. What relation are Bethany and Lewis to Clark?
11. What happens to Bethany's cat?
12. And what happens to the tree?
13. What is Clark expecting to find in the envelope when the courier arrives?
14. But what is it instead?
15. What does Clark wish he could do, which Eddie takes literally?
16. And what does Frank then do?

17. But Frank's wife Helen has already called someone. Who turns up?

18. The kids think they've seen Santa in the distance; Clark says it is the Christmas Star; but what does Lewis say that the light is?

19. What Christmassy character flies as the sky lights up, courtesy of Lewis's cigar again?

20. Where do the SWAT team end up?

Answers on page 289

The Nightmare Before Christmas

Please don't have nightmares, The Nightmare Before Christmas is simply a gothy, frothy and sometimes sploshy movie from the ever-reliably spooky Tim Burton. It's more cute than scary, to be honest, and the title is a typically over-the-top take on the actual plot. Do you fancy some questions?

Going for a Burton

Discuss whether *The Nightmare Before Christmas* is a Christmas movie, a Halloween film, both – or neither. You may take it in turns to convince a nominated neutral player, whose word is final. The use of props, clips, music, re-enactments, and impressions is very much encouraged.

(Or – you may just enjoy the chat!)

American Gothic

Together, rank these other Tim Burton movies from one to 10:

Edward Scissorhands
Beetlejuice
Corpse Bride
Sleepy Hollow
Dumbo
Alice In Wonderland
Frankenweenie
Miss Peregrine's House For Peculiar Children
Charlie and the Chocolate Factory
Mars Attacks!

Extra points: make an argument as to which movie isn't in that list, but should be

Would You Rather

Would you rather eat thirty sprout-sized Halloween pumpkins, or one pumpkin-sized Christmas sprout?

Would you rather have a Halloween-themed Christmas, or a Christmas-themed Halloween?

20 Questions

1. What is the name of the animation technique used to create the movie?
   a. Stop. Click. Shoot
   b. Stop-motion animation
   c. AI CGI

2. What is the name of the main character?
   a. Jack Skellington
   b. Jackson Browne
   c. Halloween Jacko

3. And which town is he the king of?
   a. Skellingtown
   b. Pirate Vale
   c. Halloween Town

4. How many magic doors in trees does Jack encounter in the woods?
   a. 3
   b. 10
   c. 7

5. Who is secretly in love with Jack?
   a. Santa
   b. Sally
   c. Oogie Boogie

6. When he says 'the whole thing starts with a box', what does Jack mean?
   a. A pizza delivery
   b. A present
   c. A boxing match

7. Which animal's breath does Sally say, 'overpowers any odour'?
   a. Platypus
   b. Dragon
   c. Frog

8. According to Sandy Claws, who never receives presents?
   a. Naughty children
   b. Unwashed dogs
   c. Skeletons

9. What is the name of the mad scientist in the movie?
   a. Doctor Foster
   b. Doctor Frankenstein
   c. Doctor Finkelstein

10. Mega-prolific legendary composer Danny Elfman wrote the music for the movie and also provided Jack Skellington's singing voice. Can you name the very famous long-running animated TV series he also wrote the theme tune for?
   a. *Spongebob Squarepants*
   b. *Peppa Pig*
   c. *The Simpsons*

11. The Canadian actor playing Sally has also appeared in another Christmas movie, *Home Alone*. She also worked with Tim Burton on the film *Beetlejuice* and has a long and successful acting and comedy career. But can you name her?
   a. Catherine The Great
   b. Catherine O'Hara
   c. Marjory Dawes

12. What is the shape of the head of the Mayor of Halloween Town?
    a. Square
    b. Circle
    c. Triangle

13. And what does he have instead of a bow tie?
    a. A snake
    b. A spider
    c. Nothing

14. What are the names of Oogie Boogie's little henchmen?
    a. Cuthbert, Dibble, and Grubb
    b. Lock, Shock, and Barrel
    c. Kevin, Stuart, and Bob

15. What colour and shape is Zero the ghost dog's nose?
    a. A red traffic light
    b. A blue lightning bolt
    c. An orange jack-o-lantern

16. What are the names of the major video game spinoffs from the movie? No multiple choice here, but a point for each correct answer.

17. After Oogie Boogie is defeated, what yucky things are shown to have been inside him?
    a. Memories of a dark past
    b. A bunch of bugs
    c. Mouldy sprouts

18. Tim Burton produced the movie, but what is the name of the director?
    a. Henry Celiac
    b. Harry Celery
    c. Hieronymous Bosch

19. There have been collectors' card games, party games and even Jenga sets released based on *The Nightmare Before Christmas*, but what was unique about the card game (and guidebook) released in 2020?
    a. All the cards were round
    b. There were no jokers
    c. It was a tarot card deck

20. And what is the name of the 2022 novel which has Sally as the main character?
    a. *Long Live The Pumpkin Queen*
    b. *Return of the Jack-y*
    c. *Sally Goes Batty*

Answers on page 291

The Polar Express

Choo! Choo! Choo! Choo! That's the sound of the police, except if they were on trains instead of in cars with sirens blaring. We're not sure that KRS-ONE would have had as much success using that form of transport in his hit single, of course. Anyway. Here's some questions and challenges about a rather excellent movie.

Impossible Challenge

Name a bad movie that Tom Hanks has been in.

The Great Game of Train

Here is our Christmas gift to you, folks. A wonderful game, invented by the author's late brother Daniel. It is simple – and yet competitive. Fun, and yet demanding close attention.

How to play: When on a long car/bus journey, the first person to spot a train must immediately shout 'TRAIN'. They then gain a point. You must spot it first, and it cannot be in a station. Someone else must verify the sighting, or it does not count. At least part of the train must be visible (for the sighted version – for the non-sighted version, distinctive train noises must be similarly verified).

The game continues until the journey ends. Everyone can play, with the exception of the driver for obvious reasons. The game of Train is clearly destined to become a national pastime that will surpass the entirety of the football Premiership, the World Cup and the Baseball World Series (comprised of teams in America and Canada). Indeed, given the long travel times of the latter it seems clear that Train will become the national obsession of baseball fans throughout the world, wherever it is played (America and Canada).

20 Questions

1. What is the narrator of the story's name (not the actor – the character)?
    a. Hero Boy
    b. Pants Man
    c. Gerard Bum

2. Where does the conductor of the train say the train is going to?
    a. The Magical Land of Chocolate
    b. Natakomi Plaza
    c. The North Pole

3. A boy called Billy isn't sure about getting on the train, which starts to leave without him. But what happens?
    a. There is a car chase and Billy jumps on
    b. The main character pulls the emergency brake so Billy can get on
    c. The train goes into reverse to pick Billy up

4. What beverage is in the cups that the dancing waiters serve the kids?
    a. Mulled wine
    b. Sunny D
    c. Hot chocolate

5. Why do the boys think that the girl might be thrown off the train?

a. Her ticket is actually for an Espresso cafe in Poland
b. Her ticket has been left on the seat and not been stamped – and then blown out the window
c. She keeps shouting 'Trains smell of poo and wee' all the time

6. So where does the Conductor take her?

a. On top of the train, flouting all health and safety guidelines
b. To see the Big Bad Wolf who is driving the train
c. Down to Acupulco, where they go loco

7. When looking for the girl and the Conductor, who does Hero Boy meet?

a. Arnold Schwarzenegger, filming his own Christmas chase movie
b. A mysterious Hobo who says he owns the train – and owns the North Pole
c. A hundred mirror images of himself, who start to fight him

8. When the boy gets to the front of the train, who does he find driving it?

a. The girl
b. Danny DeVito
c. Seventeen badgers

9. The train stops to allow an animal to cross in front of it. Do you know what animal it is?

a. Caribou
b. Crocodile
c. Crab

10. What item does Smokey use to repair the main throttle, on the ice?

a. A banana
b. Two bananas
c. A hairpin

11. Where does the Conductor take the two children after this?

a. The carriage of a thousand candy canes
b. The fitness centre of a million hunks
c. The room of abandoned toys

12. And what spooks Hero Boy there?
   a. A life-size puppet of Gordon Ramsay
   b. Sixteen ferocious honey badgers
   c. A puppet of Ebenezer Scrooge, animated by the Hobo

13. What do the boy, the girl and Billy view in the sky as they approach the North Pole?
   a. Santa's sleigh up on blocks in a magic garage
   b. The aurora borealis (northern lights)
   c. An enormous branch of Tesco Metro

14. Most of the kids get off the train to queue up for Santa's gifts. But who stays on?
   a. Joey Jo-Jo Junior Shabadoo
   b. Billy
   c. A cow called Pingu

15. Disaster! The carriage is rolling away down the hill! How does it eventually come to a stop?
   a. It crashes into an orphanage, which explodes, but Bruce Willis saves all the kids
   b. As entropy dictates, all things tend toward chaos and so the molecules in it return to their constituent atomic states
   c. Hero Boy puts the brakes on as the carriage stops on a turntable

16. What is the name of the type of aircraft that will carry the presents?

a. Zeppelin
b. Purple
c. Sabbath

17. Hero Boy cannot at first hear the bell. How does he eventually hear the beautiful tinkle?

a. He takes out his air pods, on which he'd been listening to Slayer all through the movie
b. He believes in Santa Claus, and then he can hear the lovely sound
c. He turns up the bell, which was set to mute by one of the elves by mistake

18. He cannot however later show the bell to the elves. Why?

a. It has fallen out of a hole in his pocket
b. They cannot see metal things
c. His hand has turned into sausages

19. It's Christmas Day! Hero Boy and his sister Sarah open presents! What does the boy find, to his delight?

a. The latest X-Box
b. The latest eggs box
c. The bell, which had fallen onto Santa's sleigh

20. The adults think the bell's broken. Why?
    a. They are suspicious about its ding and dong
    b. They don't believe so cannot hear it
    c. It radiates a strange glow that turns their skin invisible

Answers on page 292

The Princess Switch

Ah, we love a bit of whimsy, and if there was ever a movie that defined that word it has to be The Princess Switch. *Surely we've all daydreamed about swapping lives with a superstar for a day or two once upon a time, after all.*

What if…

Who would you want to change lives with, and why? Which of your friends/family looks like someone famous? And what would they do if suddenly they had to live that famous person's life? Extra fun for acting out scenes that might crop up if, say, that person had to present the TV show that their doppelganger starred in.

Which two famous people resemble each other? What would happen if they swapped?

20 Questions

1. Which Mark Twain novel is the idea of switching a royal and a commoner based on?
2. In which European country was *The Princess* mostly shot?
3. What is Stacy's job?
4. What is the name and title of Stacy's doppelganger?
5. And who plays both that character and Stacy in the movie?
6. Why does the royal character say she wants to switch places with Stacy?
7. What seals the deal for an initially reluctant Stacy?
8. What is the name of Prince Edward's driver, who King George sends to spy on Stacy?

9. What does Stacy's baking competitor, Brianna, do in order to sabotage the former's chances?
10. But how does Stacy react?
11. How does the Queen of Belgravia find out about the swap?
12. And how does she ensure that Prince Edward and Lady Margaret end up at the contest instead of herself?
13. Stacy and Kevin win – but that puts them in the spotlight with major consequences. What do people see for the first time?
14. Margaret is undeterred, and freed. What does she say?
15. Stacy is less confident and walks away. Why?
16. But what does Edward suggest?
17. Who catches the bouquet?
18. How many movies are there in *The Princess Switch* series?
19. A point for each: name the others.
20. Which member of the cast is producer on those sequels?

Answers on page 292

The Santa Clause

The Santa Clause – always a bone of contention in certain circumstances. Tim Allen's hapless Scott Calvin becomes entangled in a bunch of intrigue and Christmas silliness when he falls foul of that legal technicality. The results are in turn hilarious, daft, heartwarming and full of love. We wouldn't expect less at this time of year, of course. Let's test our knowledge of one of the more inventive Chrimbo movies out there – don't worry, though. There's no hidden legal snags in this bunch of questions...

20 Questions

1. What is Scott Calvin's day job?
2. And what does he want his son to keep doing, in contrast to the wishes of Scott's ex-wife Laura and her new husband?
3. Where do Scott and Charlie eat that evening?
4. Why does Scott have to put on the Santa suit?
5. What is the name of the head elf?
6. When must Scott return to the North Pole?
7. How does Scott realise that it was not actually a dream?
8. Over the following year, how does Scott change?
9. What happens when he tries to dye his hair?
10. And what happens if he shaves off his beard?
11. Why is Scott angry about the toy tank advertising idea?
12. Where do kids want to sit, whilst Charlie plays football?
13. What do Laura and Neil then decide to do?
14. What object does Charlie show Scott on Thanksgiving?

15. What happens when Laura and Neil briefly leave Scott and Charlie on their own?
16. So what do Laura and Neil do?
17. Subsequently, what happens when Scott delivers presents to Laura and Neil's house?
18. After a fine and heartstring-tugging speech by Scott, what does Laura do?
19. Laura and Neil stopped believing in Santa – but how does Scott remedy this?
20. And how can Charlie always summon his dad?

Answers on page 294

Scrooged

Don't be a Scrooge, be a dude, dude. Scroogy ain't groovy, baby. Open up your mind, be nice to people and get with the programme. That ain't the Christmas spirit, bucko. Another cautionary tale for the season, with a rather neat and tidy last act. Hey, Christmas movies have to wrap it up nicely, don't they...

Which is better?

Make a case as to which is better: *A Muppet Christmas Carol*, or *Scrooged*.

Scrooge Me This

Who is the scroogiest Scrooge in your group, and why?

Telly Smelly

Which television movie that's always on at Chrimbo is the best? Why?
And which one is the worst? Extra points for how many people you can convince to come over to your way of thinking.

20 Questions

1. Which seasonal novella is the movie based on?
   a. *A Christmas Carol*
   b. *Misery*
   c. *Cheech and Chong's Smoky-Ass Xmas Yo*

2. Which legendary actor and comedian plays the main role?
   a. Bill Gates
   b. Michael Fassbender
   c. Bill Murray

3. What is the main character Frank Cross's job in the movie?
   a. TV executive
   b. Dime Store Santa
   c. Chief Ghostbuster

4. And what show is being prepared for live broadcast?
   a. A fully-live version of *Twins*
   b. An animated version of *Sesame Street*
   c. A live production of *A Christmas Carol*

5. What is the surname of Eliot, who Frank fires?
   a. Smallbone
   b. Kilmister
   c. Loudermilk

6. Tough one, but which actor, writer, and comedian plays Eliot?
   a. Benedict Cumberbatch
   b. Bobcat Goldthwait
   c. Bifidus Digestivum

7. And which iconic character does that actor play in the *Police Academy* series?
   a. Zed
   b. General Zod
   c. Zod Oeuf

8. When Frank is visited by the ghost of his old mentor, Lew Hayward, where does Lew say his success and prestige ended?

a. At the end of a terrible movie
b. On the 14th hole, where he dropped dead
c. Pennsylvania

9. Who does Lew phone, who subsequently comes to visit Frank on set?

a. Chuck Norris
b. President Calvin Coolidge
c. Frank's ex-girlfriend, Claire Phillips

10. But when that person visits Frank, what happens?

a. Frank snubs them, saying he is too busy
b. Frank puts them in the production as an extra
c. Frank drives a Yank Tank to the bank for a prank

11. In what guise is the Ghost of Christmas Past?

a. Someone with a bedsheet over their head, and two eyeholes cut out with scissors
b. A taxi driver
c. Frank's twin sister, Francine

12. And the Ghost of Christmas Present?
   a. A fairy
   b. Slimer
   c. A great big pig

13. The Ghost of Christmas Future looks like…?
   a. The Devil
   b. Dean Martin
   c. The Grim Reaper

14. In that alternative future, what has happened to Claire?
   a. She has turned into a frog
   b. She hates Christmas
   c. She now hates the homeless

15. What does Frank do that surprises the drunken, murderous Eliot?
   a. Shows him how to dance the 'Macarena'
   b. Offers him a much better job than his old one
   c. Takes off his clothes and runs around shouting 'Elvis is a big plop'

16. The show is under way – but what does Frank do?
    a. Jumps in front of the camera, apologising to everybody and talking about life's preciousness
    b. Hides underneath the Christmas tree, and trips up Santa Claus
    c. Takes a box of matches and begins to burn everything down

17. As a result, what does Claire do?
    a. She turns her TV off and plays *Crash Bandicoot* on her PS1
    b. She runs to the nearest nunnery and signs up
    c. She rushes to the set and reunites with Frank

18. Who speaks for the first time in the movie at this point?
    a. Calvin, who has been mute since his father was murdered
    b. Father Jack, who has spent most of the film drunk on whiskey
    c. An animatronic giant Rudolph, which had been broken for decades

19. And what does that person remind Frank to say?
    a. 'God, this is boring'
    b. 'God bless us, every one'
    c. 'Go go gadget Christmas'

20. What song does the ensemble sing, led by Frank?
    a. ‘Please Please Me’
    b. ‘God Rest Ye Merry, Gentlemen’
    c. ‘Put a Little Love in Your Heart’

Answers on page 295

Shaun the Sheep: The Flight Before Christmas

Animated animal antics of the best kind here, with the seasonal hilarity turned up to maximum in a film that really does have something for all the family. That's the thing about the best animations – they're not just for kids. Every joke has a truth hidden inside it, and that's what makes for a great viewing experience. But how about a quizzing experience? Let's find out...

What Would You Do

...if you lived on a magic farm?

...if you were a farmer and had sheep that could do all this amazing stuff?

...if your fizzy pop suddenly exploded all over the room you were in?

Challenge

Create a stop-motion animation of your own using things you can already find in your house – or an entirely virtual one. You may use a phone app, of course.

Or

If you were going to make an animation in the style of *Shaun the Sheep*, what would be the plot? Would you make it about real animals, or made-up creatures, or both? Who would be in it? And who would provide the music, voices, and so on? Would it be on TV, or in the cinema?

Challenge 2

How many farm animals can you name in one minute, without repeating yourself, or stopping, or going off on a tangent?

20 Questions

1. In which popular series of animations do we first encounter Shaun?

   a. *South Park*
   b. *Wallace and Gromit*
   c. *Tellytubbies*

2. Which UK production company made it?

   a. Aardvark And Sons
   b. Aar Kid And Cilla
   c. Aardman Animations

3. What is the name of the farm?

   a. Mossy Bottom
   b. Grassy Bumbum
   c. Manor Farm

4. And the name of the farmer?

   a. Charlie Farmalot
   b. The Farmer
   c. Frances Farmer

5. Why do Shaun and Timmy decide to raid the farmhouse?

   a. To get bigger Christmas stockings
   b. To reach a consensus with the ruling pigs
   c. To get more Christmas dinner

6. What is the farmer cooking at that time?
    a. Fizzy pop
    b. Lamb chops
    c. Pot noodle on toast

7. Where does Shaun hide Timmy?
    a. Up the chimney
    b. In a box as a present
    c. Behind the curtains

8. How does Timmy get into the back of the truck?
    a. The farmer puts him there
    b. He jumps in
    c. Teleportation

9. And where are they all headed?
    a. The pub
    b. Christmas Island
    c. The lighting of the Christmas tree

10. What are Shaun and his chums disguised as?
    a. Snowman
    b. Snowdog
    c. Boxer, the horse

11. Why do the kids get excited to see the farmer?
    a. He has the best fizzy pop in all the land
    b. He is dressed as Father Christmas so they think he is Santa
    c. He is actually a pig in disguise as a man

12. But in the confusion, what happens to Timmy?
    a. He is expelled from the farm in a power struggle
    b. He gets lost in the big crowd of kids
    c. He is given away as a present to a little boy

13. What vehicle do the flock comandeer in the subsequent chase?
    a. A Ferrari Portofino
    b. A sleigh
    c. A hovercraft

14. What is the flock's plan to rescue Timmy?
    a. Get into the house dressed as Christmas Carollers
    b. Go down the chimney dressed as Santa
    c. Teleport into the house with a special invention

15. So how *do* they get in?
    a. Shirley through the basement, and Shaun through an air vent
    b. Shirley dressed as a pie, and Shaun by osmosis
    c. Shirley through the kitchen, and Shaun through an upstairs window

16. What does Timmy have to do when the boy opens the box?
    a. Pretend to be asleep
    b. Punch him upside the noggin
    c. Pretend to be a toy sheep

17. Why is Blitzer incapacitated at this point?
    a. He has eaten too many Christmas puddings and can't move from the sofa
    b. He has fallen into a lake and is stuck in a block of ice
    c. He is racked with confusion after seeing the pigs standing on two feet like humans

18. What is Timmy's mum's approach to getting into the house?
    a. Subtle reasoning based on logic and sound first premises
    b. She smashes the door down
    c. She waits for Father Christmas to come and asks a favour

19. Oh no! The sheep are trapped! What happens now?
    a. Santa casts a magic spell and frees everyone
    b. The neighbouring farmer, Mr. Frederick, blows up the house
    c. Blitzer, having had help from a passing bird, has gotten free, and drives the sleigh to them

20. What present does Timmy give Shaun?
    a. A very big kiss on the cheek and his eternal friendship
    b. A huge stocking, made of all the smaller stockings, and full of toys
    c. The secret to life without regrets

Answers on page 296

Shrek

A big green snotty monster. Just the right thing for the Christmas season, and we're not talking about your cousin Egbert who collects his bogies in jars and hides them under his bed. Nope, it's Shrek *we're all about right now, so let's get all about* Shrek...

The Shreks Are Alive

1. Improve a movie title by changing one of the words to 'Shrek'. For example: *The Empire Strikes Shrek; Teenage Mutant Ninja Shreks; For Shrek's Eyes Only; EveryShrek Everywhere All At Once.*

2. Improve a TV show title by changing one of the words to 'Shrek': *Ant and Shrek's Saturday Night Takeaway; Strictly Shrek Dancing; Have I Got Shreks For You; Richard Osman's House Of Shreks.*

3. Improve a song or album by changing one of the words to 'Shrek': *New York, New Shrek; Ace of Shreks; I Can't Get Shrek Out Of My Head; W.A.Shrek; I Kissed A Shrek (And I Liked It).*

Where's Shrek?

At some stage over the holiday season, try and subtly get references to the *Shrek* movies into conversations, without anyone noticing. You might, for example, refer to someone being 'as nasty as Lord Farquaad', or that your pudding is delicious 'like a Gingerbread Man', or 'as obvious a liar as Pinocchio'… it's up to you. Award yourself a point each time you get away with it, but as soon as someone picks up on what you're doing you must tell them what you're doing, and they must join you in the game. The fewer players, the more you score

– but the more players that work it out and therefore are also playing, the more fun!

20 Questions

1. If you don't know this then you've never seen the movies: who is the actor that plays Shrek?
2. And which megastar plays Donkey?
3. And who plays Princess Fiona?
4. That actress didn't provide the singing voice, though. Who did? (Clue: you're looking for two people here.)
5. And which heart-throb is the voice of Puss in Boots who first appears in *Shrek*?
6. Which swashbuckling (human) character is Puss in Boots paying homage to?
7. There have been three specifically Christmas-related short *Shrek*-world animations. Can you name them?
8. What is the catchy song that all the creatures sing at the end of the first movie?
9. And who originally released it?
10. But who wrote it?
11. In *Shrek 2*, who is trying to interfere in the Shreks' happy marriage, and why?

12. What animal does King Harold turn into at the end of that movie?
13. *Shrek the Third* now: what is the name of Fiona's cousin that will run the country if they can find him?
14. Why does Shrek think he would never be a good dad?
15. How many babies does Fiona have at the end?
16. Rather than being a terrifying ogre, what is Shrek's main occupation at the start of *Shrek Forever After*?
17. What is the catch in the deal he makes with Rumpelstiltskin, involving swapping one of his childhood days for one day as a 'real' ogre?
18. But how does Fiona break the deal, fixing things again?
19. What was the name of the TV series, tracking the adventures of Puss in Boots, which ran between 2015 and 2018?
20. Which Academy Award (Oscar) did *Shrek* win?

Answers on page 297

The Snowman

We're welling up already; The Snowman *is one of the most beautiful, gentle, lovely, and poignant animations out there. Whilst we go and find a tissue to stem the tears, the snuffles, and the snot, how about we leave some questions about this magnificent piece of work here?*

20 Questions

1. Who wrote the book from which *The Snowman* animation was developed?
   a. Raymond Briggs
   b. Ryan Giggs
   c. Ronnie Biggs

2. What is the name of the iconic song on the soundtrack, sung by a choirboy?
   a. 'All the World is Sleeping'
   b. 'Walking in the Air'
   c. 'Christmas is Great'

3. And who was that angelic vocalist, from the St. Paul's Cathedral Choir?
   a. Peter Rabbit
   b. Alex Jones
   c. Peter Auty

4. But which singer has gotten more accolades for his own version?
   a. Aled Jones
   b. Alexander Armstrong
   c. Jackanory Favabean

5. What is unusual about the animation?
   a. It has no dialogue
   b. It is in black and white
   c. It was the first AI-generated cartoon

6. What magical event happens on the stroke of midnight?
   a. The Snowman turns into a Gremlin
   b. The Snowman comes alive
   c. The Snowman's heart grows three times bigger

7. And what does the boy (who is called James) first do?
   a. Asks the Snowman for three wishes
   b. Eats the Snowman's hand
   c. Shows the Snowman around the house, playing with toys and so on

8. Where do they go next?
   a. On a sleigh ride to see Santa
   b. On a motorcycle ride through a forest
   c. On a speeder chase through Endor's forest moon

9. But what happens to the Snowman?
   a. The engine heat starts to melt him, so he has to sit in the freezer
   b. The motorbike crashes, so he turns into a snowdrift
   c. James holds him too tightly and breaks the Snowman's arm

10. Where do the friends fly to next?
    a. The South Downs, the Royal Pavilion, Brighton Pier, Norway, a forest of Snowmen, and finally to meet Father Christmas
    b. South toward London, take Junction 24 toward Ifield, grab a quick bite at the services there, and finally catch the ferry toward the Hook of Holland
    c. Lando Calrissian's Cloud City, where they are arrested by the Empire's Stormtroopers and encased in Carbonite, then sent to Jabba the Hutt as payment for an outstanding debt

11. What does Santa give to James?
    a. A lolipop, and an autographed photo
    b. Sixteen tons of No. 9 coal
    c. A card, and a snowman scarf

12. The two return home and go to sleep. But what does James find the next morning?

   a. That the Snowman has gone on holiday to Greece, leaving a note saying he'll return when it's warmer
   b. The Snowman's eyes, nose, coal buttons, hat and scarf – he has melted as the magic wore off
   c. A present from Santa, which includes a free pass to the North Pole any time he wishes

13. Which famous rock star appears in a sequence in his apparent childhood home, finding a scarf like the one James had?

   a. Elton John
   b. Lemmy from Motörhead
   c. David Bowie

14. What is the name of the 2012 sequel to *The Snowman*?

   a. *The Snowman Returns*
   b. *The Snowman and the Snowdog*
   c. *Snow is as Snow Does*

15. Billy and his mum have moved into their new house. Why is it a familiar place to us?
    a. It is where Paddington Bear also lives
    b. It is James's old house from *The Snowman*
    c. It is the Houses of Parliament

16. Why is Billy sad?
    a. He is mourning the death of his dog
    b. He doesn't like Christmas
    c. He has too much homework

17. What does he find under a loose floorboard?
    a. A million pounds in cash
    b. A voucher for *Toys R Us*
    c. A photo of James with the Snowman, plus a scarf, hat, coal and tangerine

18. So what does Billy do?
    a. Throws it all away and moves on with his life
    b. Learns to juggle and goes to join a circus
    c. Builds a Snowman and a Snowdog for himself

19. And what happens?
    a. The Snowman and a Snowdog come to life
    b. Billy becomes a television superstar
    c. Billy's mum gets a new job as snowplough driver

20. What does Father Christmas give to Billy?
   a. A voucher for *Abrakebabra*
   b. A brand-new state-of-the-art Magicsleigh X2000
   c. A magic collar which turns the Snowdog into a real, live dog

Answers on page 298

Star Wars Movies

Would it really be Christmas without all the Star Wars *movies showing on the goggly-box? No, it would not. So here's a bunch of quiz questions and some other challenges that we found in a galaxy far, far away, a long time ago.*

I Feel the Conflict

Would you rather be a Wookie or a Mandalorian?

Who's more badass – Darth Maul or Boba Fett?

Is Ren more powerful than Luke Skywalker?

The Argument

Who Shot First – Han, or Greedo?

Is Jar-Jar Binks really a malevolent Sith Lord under deep cover?

What the hell was *The Last Jedi* all about?

Why didn't Disney have a storyboard plan for VII–IX and instead seemed to (X-) wing it?

The Old Order

Make a convincing case as to which order the main, canon nine Star Wars movies should be watched in. Some suggestions to start you off:

a) Consecutively: I to IX
b) Release Order: IV–VI, I–III, VII–IX
c) The 'Machete' Order: IV, V; II, III; VI, VII, VIII, IX
d) A New Order of your own making – *you may include*

spin-offs such as Rogue One *and canon movies, but not the* Holiday Special *or the TV shows.*
e) anything goes including all TV shows, non-canon books, animations, video games, and fan-made bootlegs.

20 Movie Questions

1. When Obi Wan Kenobi said 'You will never find a more wretched hive of scum and villainy,' where was he referring to?
    a. The House of Commons
    b. Mos Eisley Spaceport
    c. The Death Star

2. Which of these is the real Yoda quote?
    a. Not to be, or to be, the question that is
    b. Stupid is as stupid does
    c. Do, or do not. There is no try

3. Which species does the junk dealer (and slave owner) Watto belong to?
    a. Kardashian
    b. Tayto
    c. Toydarian

4. What is Galactic Emperor Palpatine's first name?
   a. Sheev
   b. Ska
   c. Kenny

5. What is unusual about Darth Maul's lightsaber, in the canon movies?
   a. It is the first double-bladed one we encounter
   b. It can regenerate flesh
   c. It is carbon-neutral

6. What is Order 66?
   a. Special chow mein with barbecue sauce
   b. An instruction for all clones to turn against the 'traitorous' Jedi
   c. A protocol to protect Darth Vader's suit from high water pressure

7. What is the name of the Wookies' home planet?
   a. Kashkonverttars
   b. Kashyyyk
   c. EastEndors

8. What is the (fatal) technique used to siphon The Force from one individual to another?
    a. Riptide Force
    b. Force Lightning
    c. Force Drain

9. What is the name of the crystal inside a Jedi lightsaber?
    a. Diatium Fusion Cell
    b. Kyber
    c. Lemmy's Laser

10. Which of these is NOT a Star Wars character?
    a. Ello Asty
    b. Lembit Opik
    c. Paodok'Draba'Takat Sap'De'Rekti Nik'Linke'Ti' Ki'Vef'Nik'NeSevef'Li'Kek

11. In which modern-day Earth country is the Lars homestead (Luke's boyhood home)?
    a. Tunisia
    b. Egypt
    c. Algeria

12. What is the 'Rule Of Two'?
    a. There can only be two Jedi called Skywalker
    b. There can only be two Sith at once
    c. It is how Ren and Ben are intrinsically linked

13. What is 'Splinter of the Mind's Eye'?
    a. A blind spot in the force sensitivity of the Sith
    b. A novel initially considered as a potential sequel story to *A New Hope*
    c. A disease suffered by sub-standard Kaminoan-created clones

14. What is the artefact in the possession of Lor San Tekka?
    a. A piece of the ruined Death Star with immense powers
    b. A universal translator chip given to her by C-3PO
    c. A vital part of the map to locate Luke Skywalker

15. What does TIE in TIE-Fighter stand for?
    a. Twin Ion Engine
    b. Total Immersion Excellence
    c. The Incredible Elk

16. In *Solo*, in which three locations does Qi'ra think there may be refined coaxium?
    a. Scarif, an Imperial vault, and maybe Mercy Island
    b. Moraband, Exegol, and Imperial stores
    c. Lidd-Ull, aL-Dee, and maybe Nett-Toh

17. How did *Millennium Falcon* complete the Kessel Run in twelve parsecs?
    a. They stole a super-space speed Falcon-class disninhibitor from Jabba the Hutt
    b. They didn't – it was a lie told by Han to impress Luke and Obi-Wan
    c. They skirted close to black hole clusters, taking advantage of folds in space-time according to the theory of General Relativity

18. What perplexing oversight was there at the medal ceremony at the end of *A New Hope*?
    a. Luke and Han received medals, but Chewbacca did not
    b. R2-D2 was not present
    c. Princess Leia was wearing odd socks

19. What colour is the milk drunk by Luke at his island hideout on Ahch-To?
    a. White
    b. Purple
    c. Green

20. What is the historical significance of Maz Kanata's castle?

a. It was once the home of Darth Plagueis

b. It was built from the bones of ancient Bantha

c. It was the rumoured site of an ancient battle between Jedi and Sith

Answers on page 299

Star Wars Holiday Special

Whaddayamean, you've never heard of it? Well, the truth is that this wonderfully kitsch piece of TV film-making was shown once – and once only – on CBS. Since its 1978 airing, it has been the one and only piece of Star Wars production that has been mothballed and never seen the light of day in its entirety ever again. If you've not seen it, you've a dubious treat in store. To be fair, some parts of it including the Boba Fett section are really, really good. And, to be equally-fair, lots and lots of parts of it are very, very bad indeed. It is one of those so-bad-it's-good experiences, though not necessarily one you'd like to repeat any time soon.

As it's unavailable you'll be lucky to find it as low-quality bootlegs on various video sharing websites. Of course, as it's copyright material it's not strictly legal to seek it out so we will warn you against doing so. But, if somehow you accidentally come across it at someone else's house, for example, then it really is a Star Wars experience entirely unlike any other.

20 Questions

1. What in the name of holy heck was George Lucas *thinking*?
2. What is the main plot?
3. What is the name of Chewbacca's home planet?
4. And what is the name of the celebration?
5. Name the three other members of Chewie's family.
6. Why are Han and Chewie being chased by the Empire?
7. What is Luke doing when Malla contacts him?
8. What does Chewie's dad receive as a present?
9. How do the Chewbacca family try and distract the stormtroopers that arrive?
10. Which band is playing in said distraction?
11. How does Lumpy keep himself busy whilst the stormtroopers search?
12. What message comes on the viewing screen after this?
13. Which famous actress and singer runs the Mos Eisley cantina in this movie?
14. And how does Lumpy trick most stormtroopers into leaving?

15. What happens to the one stormtrooper who has sussed out the trick, and so stayed?
16. And how is his absence explained?
17. What colour are the robes that the family wear for the Tree of Life festival?
18. Who else do they find there?
19. What does Leia do at this point?
20. Seriously, though, how the actual *heck* was this piece of weirdness ever made?

Bonus: It was directed by Steve Binder – but do you know which truly seminal TV special he'd been involved with ten years previously?

Answers on page 299

Trading Places

An unlikely and amoral bet between two very rich old men is the basis of a roller-coaster experience. Intrigue, triumph, disaster and the human spirit are all examined here, and there's a scene with an amorous ape that when you really think about it is quite beyond the pale. Still, for a dollar let's give this one a go.

Challenge

If you could swap lives with someone, who would you choose, and why?

Never Have I Ever

One point for each. You decide if lowest or highest scorer wins! Here's some to start you off, so feel free to add your own ideas.

- ★ Made a bet
- ★ Checked the Stock Exchange
- ★ Worn a Santa costume
- ★ Pretended to be ill
- ★ Thought about cheating on a test
- ★ Met a gorilla
- ★ Worn an animal costume
- ★ Worn a business suit (or a posh one)
- ★ Met someone who is incredibly wealthy
- ★ Been to a live comedy gig
- ★ Told someone 'Merry New Year' on purpose

20 Questions

1. What is the surname of the elderly brothers who own the commodity brokerage?
2. And which iconic actor plays Louis Winthorpe III?
3. What about Billy Ray Valentine? Too easy?
4. What is the name of Louis's fiancée?

5. And what relation is she to the elderly brothers?
6. When Louis meets Billy Ray, what drastic development does he instigate?
7. But what does Clarence Beeks do to bring Louis himself down?
8. As a result, what do the brothers offer Billy Ray?
9. Louis is out of luck and out on the streets – what is the name of the prostitute that befriends him?
10. Louis then tries to frame Billy Ray. How?
11. Billy Ray overhears a vital conversation. What is it?
12. What is Clarence Beeks going to bring to the Dukes?
13. And why?
14. So what do Billy Ray, Louis and Ophelia do?
15. And how does the subsequent trading pan out? It's a touch fiddly to explain, but give it a bash!
16. And what is the bet that Louis and Billy Ray reveal they have made?
17. What does Billy Ray win from Louis in the bet?
18. Where do we next see Billy Ray, Louis, Ophelia and the butler, Coleman?

19. But where is Clarence Beeks?
20. What, according to Coleman, is the best way to hurt rich people?

Answers on page 301

While You Were Sleeping

Some movies are clearly Christmas films. Generally you'll get a variation on a few themes, such as:

- ★ *Everybody's glum, but then something magic happens*
- ★ *It snows and makes everyone feel all lovely*
- ★ *Someone who hated Christmas relents and now loves it*
- ★ *Santa Claus turns up and saves the day*
- ★ *The Christmas Spirit enters the whole village and all is A-OK*

Some movies are Christmas films by dint of happening at that time of year, and this is where the discussions and, yes, arguments can happen (c.f. Die Hard*). Now,* While You Were Sleeping *is possibly more in the latter camp than the former, which means it's a bit less beholden to the tropes in the list above. Undoubtedly, though, there's something warm and comforting about the movie that makes it an ideal early evening bit of fluffiness whilst stomachs manfully try and digest the mighty amount of scran consumed. Let's give ourselves a bit of brain food and have a quiz. (Note that these questions refer to the Nineties rom-com – not the 2017 South Korean series of the same name, though we hear great things about that too.)*

20 Questions

1. Which year was the movie released?
2. What is main character Lucy's job?
3. And at which station is she located?
4. On Christmas Day, who does she rescue, and why?
5. What does the nurse overhear Lucy say at the hospital, getting the wrong end of the stick?
6. Aghast, Lucy goes along with it when the family arrives, to avoid further upset. But she does tell the comatose Peter the truth. Who overhears her?
7. Why does that person decide to keep it to himself?
8. What does Peter's brother, Jack, spend his life doing?
9. But what does he secretly dream of doing?
10. What happens when Jack and Lucy spend time getting to know each other?
11. What present does Jack give her on the eve of the wedding, and why?
12. Who objects first in the wedding ceremony?
13. Who next?
14. Who was dashing to the ceremony to specifically object?

15. What does Lucy do?
16. When Lucy is at work later, collecting passenger tokens, which unusual object does she collect?
17. Who is it from?
18. Where do we see Lucy and Jack next?
19. And where are they going?
20. What was 'the perfect gift' that Lucy says Jack gave her?

Answers on page 303

White Christmas

They don't come more classic than this 1954 musical. Cheesy as you like, familiar as an old pair of slippers, but absolutely resonant with the ol' Chrimbo spirit nonetheless. If you remember the huge hygge craze of a few years ago, this flick is the very embodiment of the Scandinavians' cosy-and-happy concept. With added musical and dance routines, which were all the rage back then, when we all wore onions on our belts as was the style at the time...

Challenge

Sing the song 'White Christmas' – and see how far you get before you don't know what the words are. Everyone knows the first bit, but which one amongst you can take the mic through to the very end? You can all start at the same time, but you must drop out as soon as you've reached the end of your lyrical knowledge.

20 Questions

1. Surely we all know this one – which world-famous crooner plays the main character, Captain Bob Wallace?

2. Bit more tricky, perhaps. Who plays Bob's fellow performer, Private Phil Davis?

3. What happens which means Phil suggests to Bob that they become a double act?

4. What is the name of their post-war musical?

5. What is the name of the Florida nightclub at which Bob and Phil go to watch the new act of Betty and Judy?

6. The ladies are in a spot of bother with their landlord. Why?

7. The lads give Betty and Judy train tickets. Where to?

8. The four of them end up somewhere else. Where, and why?
9. At that time of year the place should be packed with tourists. But where are they all?
10. What is the name of the chap running the hotel?
11. And why is he so very anguished?
12. To cheer him up, what do Phil and Bob set up?
13. Who does Bob phone to try and get the hotelier back on track?
14. Bob rejects the plan. But Betty thinks he has agreed it. How did she know?
15. And as a result, where does Betty go?
16. Bob goes on the aforementioned show – who does he invite to Pine Tree?
17. What song do they all sing to Major General Waverly when he arrives?
18. And what do Betty and Bob do, as the performance continues (Judy and Phil do the same)?
19. What is the final song of the movie?
20. And what happens to the weather during this iconic tune?

Answers on page 304

Answers

Arthur Christmas

20 Questions

1. a
2. b
3. c
4. a
5. c
6. b
7. c
8. a
9. b
10. a
11. b
12. c
13. a
14. c
15. c
16. a
17. b
18. c
19. a
20. c

Bad Santa

20 Questions

1. They get jobs as Santa, and an elf, and rob shopping malls on Christmas Eve
2. Marcus's wife, Lois – their getaway driver
3. Bob Chipeska
4. She has a fetish for Santa Claus
5. Exploring mountains
6. In jail for embezzlement
7. Willie saw that his motel room was being raided
8. He now wants a purple elephant rather than a pink one
9. The bullies have given him a wedgie

10. Willie gives Thurman a letter, to pass on to the police, explaining what is going to happen on Christmas Eve
11. A home-made wooden pickle
12. He wants half of the proceeds of their scheme, to keep quiet
13. They kill Gin so they can keep all the money
14. Thurman says that he knew already, but was hoping Willie might get him a present anyway as they are friends
15. Marcus was planning to kill Willie too
16. A pink (not purple) elephant
17. He is shot by police before he can reach Thurman's front door
18. Thurman gave the police Willie's letter, which exonerated him
19. A police sensitivity counsellor
20. She is Thurman's guardian and will also look after the house

Batman Returns
20 Questions

1. Tim Burton (Seasonally-themed films include *The Nightmare Before Christmas, Edward Scissorhands*)
2. Michael Keaton
3. Michelle Pfeiffer
4. Danny DeVito

5. Red Triangle Gang
6. Max Shreck
7. He 'rescues' the Mayor's baby – but it was all staged to make him look good
8. Oswald Cobblepot
9. Pushing her out of a window
10. Numerous canvas awnings slowed and softened her descent
11. She destroys her apartment and makes herself a catsuit
12. By blowing up his company building
13. This time, it's a truck that breaks her fall
14. He plays incriminating comments by Penguin, slagging off Gotham, over the PA system
15. Penguin's Herod-esque revenge will be to kidnap the first-born sons of prominent citizens, and drown them in toxic waste!
16. An army of penguins armed with rockets
17. Four – but only in her limbs so she survives
18. She overloads the generator which explodes
19. With his umbrella gun – but he's picked up the wrong one, and it's harmless
20. Catwoman! She's not used up her nine lives (count them in the movie!)

Bridget Jones's Diary
20 Questions

1. c
2. a – clearly a reindeer and *not* a moose, just look at it. And later, Darcy even says it's a *reindeer* jumper, so there
3. b
4. c
5. a
6. b
7. b
8. c
9. a
10. c
11. c
12. b
13. a
14. c
15. b
16. a
17. c
18. a
19. b
20. c

Christmas Animations
20 Questions

1. a
2. A point for each: *Ice Age; The Meltdown; Dawn of the Dinosaurs; Continental Drift; Collision Course; The Ice Age Adventures of Buck Wild.* (The names may be prefixed with the words 'Ice Age')
3. *A Mammoth Christmas*
4. b – give a discretionary point to any smartypants who knows that *The Simpsons* began as a segment on *The Tracey Ullman Show* in 1987

5. c
6. b – the pair fail to win any money at the greyhound track and are followed home by the terrible racer – but lovely pet – Santa's Little Helper, who becomes a loved member of the Simpsons clan
7. a
8. a
9. c
10. a
11. A (Christmas) poo! Euw!
12. b
13. The Canadian Prime Minister orders all Canadians in the US to return home
14. To kill Santa Claus! Noooooo!
15. a
16. c
17. *Peanuts*
18. b
19. Linus, who reminds him of what Christmas is all about in a speech
20. a – though let's face it, we'd all love to hear the gang sing the Motörhead classic of c). A bonus point if anyone wants to Christmas-ise 'Ace of Spades'

Deck the Halls

20 Questions

1. Danny DeVito
2. Arnold Schwarzenegger – in *Twins*
3. Matthew Broderick
4. *Ferris Bueller's Day Off*. The car was a 1961 Ferrari 250 GT California Spyder
5. His own boss!
6. He wants to make the house visible from space, using Christmas lights
7. Horses from Buddy's display get spooked by the flash and Steve is taken literally for a ride
8. In one of Buddy's light show set pieces the doors get ripped off
9. Buddy's petrol chainsaw spills onto it and it goes on fire
10. Packing the fuse box with snow
11. Buddy has an extra power generator, which kicks in
12. They will contest the Winterfest speed-skating race. If Steve wins, Buddy takes the lights down. If Buddy wins, Steve has to buy Buddy a car
13. The house still cannot be seen from space
14. Buddy takes his wife's expensive vase to a pawn-broker, to pay for a huge amount of new LED lights
15. The Atomic Warlord
16. He hits the town's Christmas tree – which goes on fire

17. He has been using Steve's electricity
18. By creating a lovely winter wonderland, and making a delicious meal
19. They wave flashlights and sing carols in a very Christmassy way
20. The reporter says that the lights – and therefore the house – can now actually be seen from space

Die Hard
20 Questions

1. b
2. c
3. b
4. b
5. a
6. c
7. c
8. c
9. a
10. c
11. c
12. b
13. c
14. c
15. b
16. c
17. b
18. c
19. c
20. a

Doctor Who Christmas Specials
20 Questions

1a: 1965
1b: 'The Feast of Steven'
1c: The First Doctor, William Hartnell

Bonus: K9; *K9* and *Company*; 'A Girl's Best Friend' (an extra billion geek points for knowing it was K9 Mark III)

2. The Doctor is out of action as he is recovering from a traumatic regeneration
3. Blood control – specifically all those with A Positive type
4. 'Don't you think she looks tired?'
5. Get married! She was actually being escorted down the aisle by her father
6. A Racnoss spaceship
7. He seems to have no emotional reaction; this is entirely at odds with his avowed status as respecter of life (Daleks aside, natch)
8. The TARDIS hull is breached, having been crashed into by a spaceship replica of the *Titanic*
9. Everyone has left for Christmas as they are scared that aliens always seem to attack!
10. By reconstituting her pattern from the teleport system – but it is too damaged so only a shadow can be generated, and after he kisses her goodbye she becomes tiny sparks of light that diffuse throughout the universe
11. 1851
12. The Cybermen
13. He sends the CyberKing into the Time Vortex
14. The Master – specifically the Saxon Master
15. The paradox would rip the Time Vortex apart and time would cease to be

16. 'Geronimooooooo'
17. Matt Smith
18. How many days she has left to live
19. They are sharks
20. Well, you lovely and lucky person – there's one out right now cause we published it!

Edward Scissorhands
20 Questions

1. His inventor died before he could give Edward the hands he'd made
2. Vincent Price
3. Peg Boggs, an Avon saleswoman
4. Bill, her husband; her son, Kevin; and her daughter, Kim
5. By throwing a barbeque so he can meet them all
6. He trims their hedges into beautiful shapes (topiary)
7. Dog grooming, and hairdressing
8. Joyce
9. She attempts to seduce him; Edward is very naive and incapable of responding how she hoped
10. To pick a lock
11. That Edward has no common sense and is very naive from being alone for so long
12. He makes an ice sculpture, an angel based on Kim. The speed at which he works makes ice shavings fly into the air and fall as 'snow'

13. He distracts Edward, who accidentally cuts Kim's hand
14. In anger, he destroys all his works
15. He does not in case he hurts her
16. He cuts Kevin by accident when pushing him out of the way of a car driven by a drunken and raging Jim
17. He brings a gun and confronts Edward again
18. Jim slaps Kim
19. That they have killed each other
20. That she is Kim. Extra points for explaining that: she has never seen Edward again; as he is a created being she believes he may be immortal and thus still alone in his castle; there is occasional snow which she believes is from his ice sculptures

Elf

20 Questions

1. b
2. a
3. c
4. a
5. b
6. c
7. a
8. a
9. a
10. c
11. a
12. c
13. a
14. c
15. b
16. c
17. c
18. c
19. b
20. c

Frozen
20 Questions

1. c
2. c
3. b
4. a
5. b
6. b
7. c
8. c
9. a
10. a
11. c
12. a
13. a
14. b
15. b
16. a
17. a
18. a
19. c
20. b

Gremlins
20 Questions

1. a
2. b
3. b
4. c
5. a
6. c
7. b – but in *Gremlins 2* the movie does poke fun at this, much like answer c
8. a
9. c
10. c
11. b
12. a
13. c
14. a
15. c
16. b
17. c
18. b
19. c – and an extra point for spotting composer Jerry Goldsmith in there too!
20. a

Bonus answer: Because both films had a little more violence than was usual in PG-rated movies, but were not considered 'adult' enough for the 18 (restricted age) rating, Spielberg amongst others suggested there ought to be a brand new rating between PG and R. The Motion Picture Association of America agreed, and within a couple of months duly introduced an intermediary rating of PG-13

The Grinch
20 Questions

1. Dr. Seuss
2. Theodor Seuss Geisel
3. Accept all these answers: *How the Grinch Stole Christmas; Dr. Seuss's How the Grinch Stole Christmas; The Grinch (UK)*
4. Jim Carrey
5. Anthony Hopkins
6. Whoville
7. It was two sizes too small
8. Max
9. 53
10. Fred
11. The orphanage where he was as a child
12. Santa Claus
13. 'Welcome Christmas'
14. It triples in size

15. Fred (and his family)
16. Benedict Cumberbatch
17. Believe it or not, it's 600 million – that's a LOT of rhymes!
18. 236! It was a challenge by an education director called William Ellsworth Spaulding of Houghton Mifflin. Spaulding had made a list of 348 words that first-graders should be able to read, and told Dr. Seuss to write a book using only 250!
19. Zoice, or Soice, (rhyming with 'rejoice') – but actually most people pronounce it 'Seuss' (to rhyme with 'goose') and the author himself also came to use that pronunciation for rhyming reasons – so either answer gets a point!
20. A point for each: Theophrastus Seuss; Theo LeSieg; Rosetta Stone are the main ones. He is also said to have written as L. Pasteur; DG Rossetti; Seuss, for his college magazine

Harry Potter
20 Questions

1. Joanne
2. Kathleen
3. 8
4. *Harry Potter and the Philosopher's Stone; Harry Potter and the Chamber of Secrets; Harry Potter and the Prisoner of Azkaban; Harry Potter and the*

Goblet of Fire; Harry Potter and the Order of the Phoenix; Harry Potter and the Half-Blood Prince; Harry Potter and the Deathly Hallows Part 1; Harry Potter and the Deathly Hallows Part 2

5. Daniel Radcliffe
6. Emma Watson
7. Rupert Grint
8. Lord Voldemort
9. Quidditch
10. He is 11
11. It can turn any metal to gold, and also help create an immortality elixir
12. Richard Harris, who passed away after *Chamber of Secrets*. He was replaced by Michael Gambon subsequently
13. Jude Law
14. *Hogwarts Legacy*
15. *Magic Beyond Words: The JK Rowling Story*
16. She said the idea of watching it made her 'curl up like a pretzel'. She also noted that she was there at the time, so why would she want to watch someone else's version of her life. Fair enough
17. Muggles
18. Horcrux
19. By committing murder
20. It is Harry Potter himself

The Holiday
20 Questions

1. b
2. a
3. a
4. c
5. a
6. b
7. b
8. c
9. a (you could argue that technically b also works, but not in the world of this movie)
10. a
11. b
12. b
13. b
14. a
15. a
16. c
17. b
18. b
19. a
20. c

Home Alone
20 Questions

1. c
2. a
3. b
4. :)
5. a
6. b
7. b
8. c
9. c
10. b
11. c
12. c
13. a
14. c
15. a – a bonus point for correctly identifying that Kieran is Macaulay's real-life brother
16. b
17. c

18. b
19. c
20. b. Best Original Song; and Best Original Music. But the movie did not win either category

It's a Wonderful Life
20 Questions

1. George Bailey
2. James Stewart
3. *The Greatest Gift* by Philip Van Doren Stern (1943). Extra points for knowing author and year!
4. *A Christmas Carol* by Charles Dickens (1843)
5. Ending it all by jumping off a bridge
6. His guardian angel (second class), Clarence Odbody. Again, points for each piece of info
7. He saves his little brother, Harry, from drowning
8. George stops Mr. Gower the pharmacist ruining a prescription which would have accidentally poisoned the recipient
9. He must run the family banking business after a board vote
10. Harry has already accepted a job from his new father-in-law
11. Loses $8,000 which the greedy profiteer Henry Potter keeps, putting the company into huge trouble
12. Potter says George is worth more dead than alive
13. Pottersville (and not a wizard in sight)

14. In jail, for manslaughter – George did not alert him to the accidental poisoning
15. Harry drowned without his brother to save him. As a result, Harry was not able to save troops in the war so they were also lost
16. Mary does not know who George is, and runs away in terror
17. Uncle Billy and Mary have mobilised Bedford Falls' population. Because they all love George they have donated everything they can, and the $8,000 and more is covered as a result
18. *The Adventures of Tom Sawyer* by Mark Twain. (Give a point for smartypants people who know that Twain's real name was Samuel L. Clemens)
19. 'Remember, no man is a failure who has friends. Thanks for the wings!'
20. A bell rings on the Christmas tree. According to Zuzu Bailey (George's youngest daughter), every time a bell rings, an angel gains their wings. George's response: Atta boy, Clarence!

Jack Frost
20 Questions

1. b
2. a
3. a
4. b

5. a
6. a
7. c
8. a
9. b
10. a
11. b
12. a
13. b
14. a
15. c
16. a
17. c
18. c – extra points for knowing they are Dweezil, Moon Unit and Ahmet Zappa
19. c
20. Our money'd be on b, but the only points on offer here are for entertaining answers and convincing arguments, with the casting vote given by the questionmeister on the day

James Bond
10 Silly Questions

1. Tennish
2. James Pond
3. Roger Moore
4. Daniel Craig

5. Chubby Broccoli
6. Because he was shaken, not stirred
7. There was a really big Q
8. Eminem (M and M)
9. Because they heard 'You Only Live Twice'
10. Jaws

And 10 Sensible Ones

1. Ian Fleming
2. Kingsley Amis (as Robert Markham); Raymond Benson; Christopher Wood (novelisations of *The Spy Who Loved Me* and *Moonraker*); John Gardner; Sebastian Faulks; Jeffery Deaver; William Boyd; Anthony Horowitz
3. Charlie Higson. In 1967 a book called *The Adventures of James Bond Junior, 003 ½,* was released under the pseuydonym R.D. Mascott. Its author has been variously named as Roald Dahl, Kingsley Amis, and Arthur Calder-Marshall. Calder-Marshall was confirmed as author on his 1992 death
4. *The Moneypenny Diaries*
5. Samantha Weinberg
6. 11 November – there is much discussion as to whether this is 1920 or 1921
7. Sean Connery

8. *Goldfinger, The Man with the Golden Gun,* and *Goldeneye*
9. Billie Eilish, for the theme of *No Time To Die* (2020). She was 18 years old
10. 'Goldfinger', 'Moonraker', and 'Diamonds Are Forever'

Jingle All the Way
20 Questions

1. Turbo-Man
2. Minneapolis (and also St Paul, its twin city)
3. His son Jamie's karate event
4. His wife Liz had told him two weeks prior, but he forgot
5. Myron Larabee
6. In a dodgy warehouse full of counterfeits
7. The police raid the facility and a fight breaks out
8. Howard claims that he is an undercover cop
9. Holiday Wintertainment Parade
10. A Johnny Seven OMA (One Man Army). In other words, a big toy gun
11. They hear a radio DJ advertise one in a competition
12. It is actually a gift certificate for the toy, not an actual physical one
13. Myron produces a letter bomb which he says is not real (but it actually does detonate on Officer Hummell). Different times, folks. Different times

14. It has been stripped down by car thieves so he has to go home in a tow truck
15. He plans to steal his neighbour's Turbo-Man toy, bought for their own kid, from the neighbour's house
16. Although Howard has not actually stolen anything, he has been caught in a compromising position. The family are disgusted so go with Ted, the neighbour
17. Ted makes a pass at Liz, which she rebuffs in disgust
18. He has run onto Officer Hummell again
19. In brief: Howard is mistaken for the Turbo-Man actor; he dons the suit; Howard then starts to give Jamie a Turbo-Man toy; Myron however turns up in a Dementor costume (Turbo-Man's enemy); the two have a long and noisy fight with jetpacks and all manner of craziness; Myron steals the toy from Jamie; Howard apologises to his family; the police give Jamie the toy back; Jaime gives it to Myron for his son and says Howard is 'his real hero'. Roll credits (more or less) – phew!
20. Liz asks Howard what he has gotten her for Christmas – and he clearly has forgotten to get her anything in the excitement (and also because he ought to have shopped two weeks earlier, avoiding this whole mess. Mind you, the movie'd probably not be quite as exciting if he had)

Klaus

20 Questions

1. a
2. b
3. c
4. b
5. c
6. a
7. c
8. b
9. a
10. b
11. c
12. a
13. b
14. c
15. a
16. b
17. a
18. c – but of course, answer a is also correct in one sense
19. c
20. a

Krampus

20 Questions

1. c
2. a
3. b – German for 'grandmother'
4. c
5. c
6. a
7. a
8. a
9. c
10. b
11. b
12. c
13. c
14. a
15. a
16. c
17. a
18. a
19. b
20. c

Last Christmas
20 Questions

1. b
2. a
3. c
4. b
5. b
6. c
7. b
8. a, b, and c :)
9. b
10. a
11. b
12. a
13. b
14. a
15. b
16. c
17. a
18. b
19. b
20. b

Love Actually
20 Questions

1. Richard Curtis
2. 'Love Is All Around' (Bonus point for getting the original band: The Troggs **not** Wet Wet Wet)
3. 'Christmas Is All Around'
4. Elton John
5. 'All You Need Is Love' (Bonus point: by the Beatles)
6. He comes to her house with a ghetto blaster and a bunch of statements written on pieces of card
7. Portuguese
8. A French cottage
9. A design agency
10. She is his secretary/assistant

11. A necklace with a gold heart
12. A CD by Joni Mitchell
13. Her brother
14. Prime Minister of the UK! (If you don't get this right, have you even *seen* the movie?)
15. Joanna – also the name of his late mother
16. He runs through airport security to let her know!
17. In a psychiatric institution
18. He panics, wishes her Merry Christmas, and leaves her in tears. Booooo!
19. His English accent
20. 4
21. Doing sex scenes in movies
22. Working Title Films
23. Bill Nighy
24. Best Supporting Actor
25. 'Red Nose Day Actually'

Miracle on 34th Street
20 Questions

1. c
2. a
3. b
4. a
5. b
6. a
7. a

8. c
9. b
10. b
11. c
12. a
13. a
14. c
15. a
16. b
17. a
18. c
19. a
20. b

The Muppet Christmas Carol
20 Questions

1. Gonzo
2. Rizzo the Rat
3. Michael Caine
4. Kermit the Frog
5. Dr. Bunsen Honeydew and Beaker
6. That the poor people are already served by prisons and workhouses, and that if they die there will be a decrease in 'surplus population'. What a cad!
7. Robert – as in Robert Nesta Marley, better known as Bob Marley
8. Statler and Waldorf

9. Belle
10. The one, the only Miss Piggy
11. Robin
12. Seeing that people rejoice in his demise, and viewing his own headstone
13. Bean Bunny
14. That Bob will get a raise, and that Scrooge will pay off Bob's mortgage
15. Sam the Eagle
16. Dr. Teeth and the Electric Mayhem
17. Animal
18. 'Thankful Heart'
19. Dickens says that Scrooge becomes like a second father to the lad
20. Tiny Tim survives and gets well again. Huzzah!

National Lampoon's Christmas Vacation 20 Questions

1. Griswold
2. Chevy Chase
3. Cornelius Crane Chase. If anyone knows that 'the Ballad of Chevy Chase' is a 16th-century folk song about a hunting party that begets an Anglo-Scottish battle, then quite frankly give them a million points and a special cake
4. Beverly D'Angelo
5. An axe or any other tree-felling equipment

6. Clark has wired up a ludicrous number of lights to the house, which draws all the juice from the grid
7. Rottweiler
8. Snots
9. In their motor home (RV), because they had to sell their home when times got tough
10. His aunt and uncle
11. Electrocuted
12. Lewis burns it down with sparks from his cigar
13. A Christmas bonus
14. Membership to a 'jelly club'
15. Clark wants to tell his boss Frank off in person, so Eddie goes and kidnaps him!
16. Frank says the proper bonus will be reinstated
17. She calls the police – and a SWAT team comes and points guns at everyone
18. He says it's from the local sewage treatment plant. How seasonal, eh
19. Lewis chucks his match into the storm drain, where Eddie's RV has been dumping sewage – and the gas explodes, launching the Santa decoration into the sky
20. They join the party at the Griswolds' house along with everyone else

The Nightmare Before Christmas

20 Questions

1. b
2. a
3. c
4. c
5. b
6. b
7. c
8. a
9. c
10. c
11. b
12. c
13. b
14. b
15. c
16. The main two games based entirely on the movie are *The Nightmare Before Christmas: The Pumpkin King* and *The Nightmare Before Christmas: Oogie's Revenge*. However, you can also accept for bonus points the *Kingdom Hearts* series as Halloween Town and Christmas Town both feature, along with several characters; this also applies to *Disney Magic Kingdoms*; *Disney Heroes: Battle Mode; Disney Sorcerer's Arena; Disney Mirrorverse* (Disney makes their IP *go to work*, yo)

17. b
18. a
19. c
20. a

The Polar Express
20 Questions

1 a
2. c
3. b
4. c
5. b – though UK passengers may have some sympathy for answer c
6. a
7. b
8. a
9. a
10. c
11. c
12. c
13. b
14. b
15. c
16. a
17. b
18. a
19. c
20. b

The Princess Switch
20 Questions

1. *The Prince and the Pauper*
2. Romania
3. A baker, in Chicago
4. Lady Margaret Delacourt
5. Vanessa Hudgens

6. She says she hates being in the spotlight, and wants to get to know what it's like to be 'a normal girl'
7. Lady Delacourt promises to secure and pay for Olivia to attend the Belgravia ballet school
8. Frank De Luca
9. Brianna messes with Stacy's equipment, specifically a kitchen mixer
10. She goes old-school and mixes the ingredients by hand instead
11. Frank shows her photographs of Margaret and Stacy together
12. The Queen pretends to be ill, so they go in her place
13. They go to get their medal – from Edward and Margaret. People see that Margaret and Stacy are identical-looking and the truth comes out
14. She tells Kevin she loves him
15. She is not comfortable in the royal life
16. He proposes marriage – if they are still in love one year down the line they will get wed
17. Lady Margaret – obviously
18. Three
19. *The Princess Switch: Switched Again; The Princess Switch 3: Romancing the Star*
20. Vanessa Hudgens

The Santa Clause
20 Questions

1. Marketing Director at a toy company
2. Scott wants Charlie to keep believing in Santa. The other grown-ups think Charlie should stop doing so
3. Denny's
4. He finds instructions on a business card, saying that if anything happened to the previous owner of the suit, it is his responsibility to complete the mission. Charlie asks his dad to do just that
5. Bernard
6. Thanksgiving
7. He is wearing the pyjamas that he was given at the North Pole
8. He puts on lots of weight and starts to crave milk and cookies
9. It turns white again
10. It grows back straight away
11. It shows Santa riding the tank, which he finds inappropriate
12. On Scott's lap – they know he's Santa
13. They get a court order from a judge to stop Scott visiting Charlie
14. A magical snow globe, given to him by Bernard
15. Bernard appears and magically brings them to the North Pole

16. They call the police, saying Scott has kidnapped Charlie
17. Scott is arrested
18. Laura burns the court documents, and says Scott can visit any time he likes
19. Scott gives them presents that they always wanted, but did not receive, which made them stop believing
20. By shaking the snow globe

Scrooged

20 Questions

1. a
2. c
3. a
4. c
5. c
6. b – extra points for knowing his real name is Robert Francis Goldthwait
7. a
8. b
9. c
10. a
11. b
12. a
13. c
14. c
15. b
16. b
17. c
18. a
19. b
20. c

Shaun the Sheep: The Flight Before Christmas
20 Questions

1. b – extra points for knowing Shaun first appeared in *A Close Shave* (1995) and in *Shopper 13* from the series *Wallace and Gromit's Cracking Contraptions* (2002)
2. c
3. a
4. b
5. a
6. a
7. b
8. b
9. c
10. a
11. b
12. c – at this point we must say that this is whimsical fictional animated entertainment, and putting animals in boxes as gifts is very much not what anyone should ever do, ever. Ever!
13. b
14. a
15. a
16. c
17. b
18. b
19. c
20. b – though the other two presents would be

wonderful. And what does the poor little boy get out of all of this, anyway? None of it is his fault. Bah – or, rather – Baaaa humbug!

Shrek

20 Questions

1. Michael Myers
2. Eddie Murphy
3. Cameron Diaz
4. Sally Dworsky for the first movie, then Renee Sands
5. Antonio Banderas
6. Zorro
7. *Shrek the Halls* (2007); *Donkey's Caroling Christmas-tacular* – also known as *Donkey's Christmas Shrektacular* (2010); *Shrek's Yule Log* (2010)
8. 'I'm a Believer'. Extra point for knowing this version was by Smash Mouth
9. The Monkees
10. Neil Diamond!
11. The Fairy Godmother is trying to break up Fiona and Shrek so that Fiona would be free to marry her son, Prince Charming
12. A frog
13. Artie
14. He is afraid he will be like his own dad – who tried to eat him!

15. Only the three little ogres :)
16. Autographing pitchforks
17. That day is the day of his birth – meaning he would never be born
18. She kisses Shrek, awwwwwwww
19. *The Adventures of Puss in Boots* (hehe)
20. Best Animated Feature

The Snowman
20 Questions

1. a
2. b
3. c
4. a
5. a
6. b
7. c
8. b
9. a
10. a
11. c
12. b
13. c
14. b
15. b
16. a
17. c
18. c
19. a
20. c

Star Wars
20 Questions

1. b
2. c
3. c
4. a
5. a
6. b
7. b
8. c
9. b
10. b
11. a
12. b
13. b
14. c
15. a
16. a
17. c (though 'b' was often cited before *Solo* showed it)
18. a
19. c
20. c

Star Wars Holiday Special
20 Questions

1. There is no actual answer to this. We doubt he even knows, himself
2. Chewie and Han are trying to get back to Chewbacca's home planet for the season
3. Kashyyyk (yes, three letter Ys in there)
4. Life Day
5. His dad, Itchy; his wife, Malla; his son, Lumpy
6. The Empire suspects there are Rebel Alliance members on Kashyyyk
7. Fixing up his X-Wing fighter spacecraft
8. A virtual reality set

9. With food, and with Malla's music video unit
10. Jefferson Starship
11. Watching a cartoon featuring Boba Fett. (This is the best bit of the whole *Holiday Special*, so seek it out)
12. That Tattoine is being put under curfew by the Empire
13. Bea Arthur – later of course seen in *The Golden Girls*
14. He has built a voice translator that mimics the stormtroopers' commander, and he uses it to tell them to return to base
15. Han uses his trusty laser gun to kill him. And, yes, he definitely shot first here too
16. Saun says that the stormtrooper had stolen supplies, and gone AWOL/deserted the unit
17. Red
18. All the gang: Luke, Leia, C-3P0, R2-D2 and Han
19. Leia makes a speech, which is not unusual, but then sings
20. Essentially, this CBS TV special was planned already. But as *A New Hope* (the original *Star Wars* movie) had been such a runaway success, the demand for a 'proper' sequel (*The Empire Strikes Back*) was huge, and so George Lucas etc went into production as quickly as possible there. Consequently, there was very little time to make this TV special, as everyone was busy with *Empire*

Bonus: The 1968 'Comeback' Special for Elvis Presley

Trading Places
20 Questions

1. Duke
2. Dan Aykroyd
3. Eddie Murphy
4. Penelope
5. Their grand-niece
6. He insists that Billy Ray is arrested for supposed theft
7. He frames Louis as a thief and drug dealer, which means he loses his job and gets thrown in jail
8. They give him Louis's job as managing director
9. Ophelia
10. By planting drugs in his desk
11. He hears the Duke brothers talking about the bet they have made: that is, to take someone from the streets and make him 'respectable', and likewise to ruin Louis's career and life
12. A special United States Department of Agriculture report on how big the orange crop will be that year
13. If they know the crop size in advance, they can buy orange juice shares before anyone else knows, and therefore control the final price. This means they'll make a fortune
14. They swap the report with a forgery
15. *Deep breath* OK… so, because the forged report says that the orange crop will be worse than usual, the Dukes buy as many frozen orange juice futures

contracts as possible. Futures means that they are committing themselves to buying actual contracts at a later date, that is, after the report is released. Because they think they know more than everyone else, they believe that they can buy a majority of orange juice contracts at a lower price than they will be worth.

Once they have all these shares they can control the price, which will be more valuable because there will apparently be a shortage of orange juice. So they will make a lot of money. This makes the rest of the stock traders also look to buy futures, which keeps driving the price up. Billy Ray and Louis sell futures contracts at a high price at this point.

When the *actual* crop report is released, showing not a shortage but a normal orange harvest, the price of the futures crashes. Billy Ray and Louis wait for a low enough price, and buy the futures at this lower price; this makes them a heck of a lot of money.

Crucially, the pair *do not* buy from the Dukes, meaning that the elderly brothers have to fulfil their commitments: this requires $394 million that the brothers do not have, effectively bankrupting them.

Our head hurts

16. That Billy Ray and Louis could become wealthy, whilst also making the Dukes poor
17. $1
18. On a tropical beach, enjoying a cool beverage

19. In the hold of a ship, dressed in a gorilla suit, with an amorous (real) gorilla suitor in the same cage
20. By turning them into poor people

While You Were Sleeping
20 Questions

1. 1995
2. Ticket/fare collector for Chicago Transit Authority. Extra point for knowing the name of her employers
3. Randolph/Wabash in Chicago
4. Peter Callaghan, who she has been admiring from afar. Muggers have pushed him onto the tracks
5. Lucy says, 'I was going to marry him', as per her long-distance admiration. The nurse takes her literally and assumes the two are engaged
6. Peter's godfather, Saul
7. The whole thing has brought the family closer together
8. Working for Callaghan and Son, the family business
9. Jack wants to be a woodworker, specifically hand-building furniture
10. Jack falls in love with her
11. A snow globe of Florence in Italy where Lucy has always dreamed of visiting
12. Lucy!
13. Jack
14. Ashley Bartlett Bacon – Peter's actual fiancée

15. She leaves the wedding as the family members all argue and kick off
16. An engagement ring
17. It's from Jack, and he proposes to her
18. Dressed in wedding clothes, on a train with a sign saying 'Just Married'
19. To Florence, for their honeymoon
20. A stamp in her passport

White Christmas
20 Questions

1. Bing Crosby
2. Danny Kaye
3. The place is bombed; Phil saves Bob's life when a wall was about to collapse on him, and gets wounded for his troubles. Bob asks how he can repay Phil, who suggests they team up
4. *Playing Around*
5. Novello's
6. The landlord is trying to sue them for a supposedly damaged rug and has even called the police about it
7. New York City
8. Pine Tree, Vermont. The women are booked to perform there
9. They have all left, because it's so warm and there's no snow
10. Major General Tom Waverly

11. He has his life savings invested in the business, and is in danger of losing it all
12. A concert at the hotel with some of the *Playing Around* actors in it
13. Ed Harrison, who has a variety show
14. Emma the housekeeper was listening to the first half of the conversation on another phone, and she told Betty
15. New York
16. The 151st Division, which was Major General General Waverly and the boys' old army division
17. 'The Old Man' (also sung to him at the start of the movie)
18. They get engaged
19. Of course it has to be 'White Christmas' :)
20. It snows, heavily and beautifully, turning Vermont and the hotel in a gorgeous and traditional Christmas Eve scene

About the Author

Joe Shooman has written words on music, entertainment, sport, news and crisps for many national newspapers and magazines over the years, and worked in radio as a presenter, producer and reporter. He is a contributor to the legendary *Viz* comic and is the author of numerous books. He once was sacked from his newspaper column for hiding rude messages about his team's rivals in the text. He lives exactly equidistant between Chibougamau, Quebec and Saryagash, Kazakhstan. Contrary to popular rumours, he does *not* like to move it, move it.